DORAN:
CHILD OF COURAGE

DORAN:
Child of Courage

———— ✳ ————

LINDA SCOTSON

Foreword by
JONATHAN MILLER

COLLINS
8 Grafton Street, London W1
1985

William Collins Sons & Co. Ltd
London · Glasgow · Sydney · Auckland
Toronto · Johannesburg

BRITISH LIBRARY CATALOGUING IN PUBLICATION DATA

Scotson, Linda
Doran: child of courage.
1. Spasticity – Patients – Biography
I. Title
362.4'3'0924   RJ496.S6

ISBN 0 00 217340 9

First published in Great Britain in 1985
© Linda Scotson 1985

Photoset in Linotron Plantin by
Rowland Phototypesetting Ltd
Bury St Edmunds, Suffolk
Made and printed in Great Britain by
William Collins Sons & Co. Ltd, Glasgow

To Lili, with love

FOREWORD
by Jonathan Miller

———❋———

For those of us who are lucky enough to get through life without any serious medical misfortune, it is impossible to imagine how someone could survive, let alone salvage anything creditable from the sort of catastrophe which Linda Scotson describes so eloquently in this admirable book.

And yet there are people – more presumably than one knows – who react to such cruel and unjust curses as if they were blessings and discover, perhaps only by hindsight, that their lives have been mysteriously enlarged and transfigured by the experience.

In refusing to accept the pessimistic verdict passed by the paediatricians on her seriously brain-damaged child, Mrs Scotson tapped unexpected sources of energy and determination which might have remained unsuspected and unexploited if she had uneventfully given birth to a normal child. But her indignant reaction was so strong, so positive, and so impatiently determined that she successfully transformed the prospects of her son and in so doing she seems to have enlarged and illuminated not only her own life but the lives of most of the people who have come in contact with her during the last five years.

Charismatic personalities of this sort are not always easy to get along with and I suspect that Mrs Scotson figures in her son's medical notes as an awkward customer and a difficult mother. As someone in other words who bloody-mindedly refuses to accept the conventional wisdom of the medical profession if she feels it is inconsistent with the best interests of her sick child. It is difficult therefore to imagine how things would have turned out if Mrs Scotson had resolutely pursued her course of visionary defiance without the help of an institution which was committed, like her, to the belief that the badly damaged nervous system could be creatively reprogrammed if only the appropriate regime of stimulation and encouragement could be designed and

7

unremittingly sustained. Mrs Scotson and her son therefore were fortunate in gaining admission to the ambitious and somewhat controversial programme which is conducted in Philadelphia by the Institutes for the Achievement of Human Potential. At the Institutes Mrs Scotson encountered an evangelical zeal which matched hers and irreversibly established the belief that Doran's cognitive and motor capabilities could be effectively redesigned in spite of the biochemical injuries which his brain had received at the time of his birth.

Inspired and encouraged by Glenn Doman, one of the co-founders of the Institutes, Linda Scotson and her son embarked on a collaborative enterprise of energetic patterning, the purpose of which was to regear the relationship between sensory input and motor output, so that Doran could effectively realise the aborted initiatives of his otherwise intact will. Orthodox neurologists have expressed serious doubts about the scientific rationale of this programme and it is not easy to decide whether the positive results constitute a reliable proof.

Nevertheless, as is often the case with unorthodox procedures, the outcome is so impressive that it would be pig-headed and narrow-minded to overlook it simply because the theory is scientifically controversial. In Doran's case his life seems to have been literally remade as a result of the efforts which have been spent on and with him, and whatever one's scientific opinion might be, however one might reflect upon the relentless ordeal to which Doran was submitted and upon the untold and unweighable sacrifices made by his normal sister, one would have to be mean-spirited and inert not to be moved and inspired by the progress which the child has undoubtedly made.

If Mrs Scotson had given birth to an uninjured baby she would in all probability have had more time to pursue her career as a talented painter and perhaps she would have fulfilled herself in the divided roles of mother and artist. But Nature frustrated this and unexpectedly forced her to combine the two roles into one. And who knows, the time may come when Linda Scotson will, like Ben Jonson, be able to point to Doran as her finest work of art.

1

EVERY CHILD has a nightmare. When I was eight years old, I found my nightmare in the place I was always happiest, the town swimming baths. I was late getting out of the water and the changing rooms had suddenly become occupied by a school party; but these children were no ordinary children. They seemed at once human and not human as they crawled, wriggled and groped their way to the side of the pool. I neither knew nor understood who they were and I ran from them not daring to look back; and yet, somehow, I was also deeply ashamed. I told no one of the fear and shame I had felt which came back inexplicably throughout my childhood.

Twenty-five years later, I was sprawled in the bedroom of a terraced cottage on the edge of a wood. I was in labour and still in love with a dead man, the father of my twenty-three-month-old daughter and of this child still struggling to be born. I held my knees and panted rhythmically while Judy, my old friend, sat up behind me. She was brave enough to let me suck her fingers which brought moisture back into my mouth. I was aware of the midwife at the foot of the bed and Judy's two daughters sitting pressed up against the dressing table; the walls and ceilings were hung with my paintings. Downstairs my daughter Lili had fallen asleep clutching a fat bunch of grapes; she was guarded by Judy's friend who had the same name as her own dead father – Peter, and his puppy, the sheep dog, Mercle. Beethoven's Triple Concerto was still faintly audible downstairs.

Since childhood I had aimed to become recognized as a painter who could present the beauty and pain of the world, I wanted to work on the frontiers of the senses. This too was a frontier, this was true and real, and it was also inescapable.

I pushed Doran into the world using the mysterious connections granted to my understanding in the act of loving his father. In the moment of triumph I felt uneasy. It seemed unreasonable, but I heard myself gasping the words, 'Is he all right?' I was sitting upright and could watch the cord being cut. I wanted things to slow down, I wanted Doran lying peacefully on my stomach. 'Doran', I had his name already, I think I had known it always. Watching the midwife work, I thought if I'd been alone I could have done it all myself, it is possible. The doctor said, 'He's very strong, he holds his head up well, Linda.'

Doran was 8lb 4oz. He looked robust, his face was full and handsome, but my anxiety could not go away. Doran did not seem like a newborn child; I would have said there was something on his mind, he kept extraordinarily awake, his eyes switched restlessly from side to side.

Everyone began gathering him up and admiring him. The midwife gave him a warm bath. I was surrounded by loving people bent upon celebration, and continuously assuring me everything was all right.

My sleeping daughter, Lili, was put to bed; doctor and midwife left; Judy stayed the night and Doran and I lay together. For a while, peace did come to me. I relaxed deeply, reunited with some element I had found and lost and had now found again. It was important to me not to let this child suffer. His father had taken on the sufferings of the world and had died. That was, I thought, enough suffering; Doran would be joyful and live joyfully.

That night Doran did not cry but he did not sleep. Morning came, Lili rushed in, scrambling happily into the bed beside her brother. Catherine, my friend for sixteen years, arrived from Liverpool. She was intending to stay the week and after hugging us all she unpacked toys, baby clothes and champagne. The sun glowed through my yellow curtains; Lili shook her yellow curls and bit into sweetcorn.

The low autumn sun spread its golden shafts into the cottage.

Doran was also yellow, so yellow that when our midwife returned she laughingly called him a 'little china man'. His urine stained his nappies yellow. The midwife seemed faintly puzzled but reassuring. 'Slight jaundice,' she said. 'May occur in normal births while the liver is still adjusting.'

'It looks a little more than slight,' I said. The midwife sighed; she would recheck our blood groups. I couldn't remember Peter's blood ever having been checked. Mine was written on the medical card staring up at her, 'A' Positive, absolutely straightforward. 'If there was an incompatibility what *would* you do?' I asked, feeling desperately hopeful that here was an excuse to do something. 'Well, we'd give him a bilirubin test. It involves taking a sample of blood from his heel; but,' she added quickly, 'they cry. Most mothers don't like it.'

I longed to prove something substantial. Quite suddenly I remembered that Peter had been a blood donor. His card lay with his passport and other personal items in a drawer by the bed. It was, I thought, an incredible piece of luck. I rummaged through the drawer and finally flourished the card. The midwife took it and opened it. 'O positive,' she smiled. 'That's very compatible, nothing to worry about.'

'But I am worried.' She smiled again, evidently trying to be kind. I felt smothered. Time passed. I did not know the implications of a blood incompatibility, and on the evidence there was no blood incompatibility. It seemed that I was incapable of asking the right questions, but before she left I tried once more to make my anxiety a reality.

'Do you think you could explain a little more about this bilirubin? I would feel a lot better if I could just understand . . .'

'It's the medical term for the yellow bile plasma which causes jaundice,' she broke in.

'But what does the jaundice do?'

'Oh, it just usually gives the baby a nice suntan for a few days, unless . . .' She paused and I felt she would have preferred not to undertake this conversation.

'Unless,' I persisted.

'Well, unless there was a blood incompatibility, and then we would have had to whip the young man into hospital for a while.'

'And what would be the worst that could happen?' I asked steadily.

She replied quickly and lightly as though to disassociate herself from the words, 'Possible brain injury. But,' she added packing up her things and moving to the door, 'thankfully we've proved there is no chance of that.'

No one around me seemed unduly disturbed. I had lost my taste for food and drink but that could be ascribed to hormone imbalance after the birth. I was advised by the doctor and midwife to give Doran plenty of fluids and not to worry unless he became drowsy. Doran did not become drowsy. He stayed awake in my arms or in Catherine's arms. He was not unduly thirsty and we had tried to spoon water into him.

On the third day after his birth it was still very warm so we sat outside the cottage and picnicked. When the midwife arrived she was horrified to find us outside in September with a newborn baby. However well bundled in blankets, the child was in danger of catching a chill. I obediently brought him inside, blinking as my eyes adjusted from the bright sunlight. On impulse, and because I could bear it no longer, I asked her to perform the bilirubin test on Doran's blood. The procedure was quick and simple and Doran's complaint was brief.

'Do you feel better now,' she asked smiling, when it was over.

I had to wait until the next day for the results. By the morning Doran was no longer awake; he was indifferent to food. He could hardly be raised from a kind of torpor. I phoned my doctor but the results had not yet arrived: I had to wait. I badly wanted to drive to the hospital there and then but the fact that a newly born child is sleeping does not usually give cause for concern.

Two hours later the phone rang, the bilirubin count in Doran's blood was dangerously high; the hospital team were prepared for an exchange transfusion. Did I want an ambulance or would I drive? All I could give my son now was speed; I would drive. I picked up Doran and virtually ordered Catherine and Lili into the car. Out of concern for our safety, Catherine climbed into the driving seat. We moved up the road with excruciating care. It was unbearable and, obedient to another command she exchanged the wheel for the increasingly stiffening body of Doran.

I drove the thirteen miles to the hospital as fast as I dared. The road is a succession of hairpin bends, hills, gradients and blind corners, but I knew it by heart.

We arrived at the appropriate entrance guided by a sympathetic angel who must have been breathing down the neck of Death and holding him off. A nurse was waiting at the door and Doran did not have his first convulsion until we were well inside the special care baby unit. While he was under observation nothing further could be done until my blood had been thoroughly tested. My blood group looked an innocent 'A' positive in every assessment. Lili, Catherine and I were left in a small consulting room with two young doctors and a large mechanical breast pump called Daisy.

They had begun to use the word 'kernicterus', which had a powerful sound. The feeling was kernicterus was now rare, so rare that Doran almost represented a piece of history. The plot, moreover, thickened because there was no evidence as to why Doran had kernicterus. The contrast between the urgency of Doran's plight and the fascinating medical conundrum it presented was almost ridiculous. I tried to make some headway.

Doran's case evidently rested on the length of time the level of bilirubin in his blood had been high. If it had not been high long then there was a chance that the brain would recover. Doran would leave the hospital whole and well and begin to enjoy the fact of having been born. We would have a great joyful celebration for him. But I knew that the level of this bilirubin was directly connected with the anxiety that had dogged my heart.

If the exchange transfusions were successful and the poison

had been washed away before any permanent harm could have been done then Doran would have escaped kernicterus. But if he had kernicterus? 'If he has kernicterus,' the doctor said, 'understand that you don't get better from kernicterus.'

'And what,' I asked, 'are its consequences?'

'Brain damage,' he answered.

Suddenly I had questions; they fell over one another. I was still looking for a way out that had been missed.

'How can you tell?' I asked. 'When can you tell? Can you tell now?'

I would have to wait. Wait for the blood transfusions. Wait for Doran's condition to settle down. Wait for the consultant pediatrician to make his rounds in about five days' time. He told me that the most striking features of kernicterus were rigidity, twitching, convulsions, restless arm movement, grunting respirations, high pitched cry and deafness. It was true that Doran already showed some of these symptoms but I hoped this was only as yet a warning . . . The two young doctors gave him a fifty-fifty chance. I saw they were being kind; for them, the choice between a dead child or a seriously brain injured child contained the morbidity of their own experience. On the surface the conversation remained positive, even cheerful in tone.

At last the consultant pediatrician arrived with his results. My blood, so apparently normal, contained a rare negative antibody in unusually high amounts – the highest on record. He was caught between the spontaneous thrill of such a discovery and the obvious disaster it now entailed. A recently fatherless family with no financial security living in a remote cottage would obviously have relied on the healthy cooperation of its remaining members. We were now dominated by the factor that united us for good or evil – blood. Biologically, Doran, Lili and I were all responsible.

I gave permission for Doran to have as many exchange transfusions as were needed to save his life. A nurse asked me Doran's religion. I said, 'He embraces all religions.'

'Oh,' replied the nurse, 'then I'll put down "Free".'

'Free,' I said, 'is appropriate.'

Catherine took Lili to stay with a young family we knew well. I had come to believe in angels and I needed them now. The doctor left me in no doubt as to the dangers of exchange transfusions and offered me a room by the maternity ward almost directly over the special care unit. They promised to call me if any 'difficulties' arose and to tell me when the transfusion was successfully over. Sleeping was impossible, so I lay down on the bed and waited. I had so much energy and I was directed to be still. It was time to survey all the material I could remember about serious brain injury. I knew this was what was very evidently promised if some intervening force did not reverse the situation. I had an idea that it would not. I had, as is common, no inspiring pictures of the results of such injury. I had seen children drooling in wheelchairs, their obscenely uncoordinated limbs thrashing about, eyes turned skywards . . . And then, as in my childhood, I was filled with fear and shame. I remembered and understood the children in the swimming baths and my shame became apparent to me. I had judged too long by appearances. It would be a lesson in love for me to have a son whose inner light must shine through a misshapen and repellent form. But for Doran himself? I could not accept it for Doran.

At this moment Doran was still beautiful, his limbs were elegantly formed, his chest was wide and his forehead broad and intelligent. His appearance contradicted his injury. I wondered stupidly how long it took an injured child to change.

At midnight two doctors appeared and reported enthusiastically that Doran had withstood the transfusions remarkably well. It had been expected that he would need five; as matters stood, he was pretty well detoxified by two. He was now having phototherapy to continue the cleaning process less traumatically.

I was still standing at the door of my room when they turned to go. In a state of panic I realized they expected me to share their relief and take advantage of some kind of sleep. I had one fixed idea.

15

'Could I see him now, please?'

They had already entered into another world. I had left their minds completely. The book of Doran was closed for the evening. Reluctantly they opened it again. 'Sleep,' they said, 'there is nothing you can do for Doran now.'

'I can't sleep. I can't sleep without seeing him. I really can't.' I foresaw to my horror that I was in danger of having an argument with the very people who had just saved my son's life. We looked at each other uncompromisingly. Rescue came from an unexpected quarter when I found myself saying, 'Basically, there's also the fact that I breast feed Doran and my breasts are really engorged now because he can't take the milk. They're jolly painful . . . Could I . . . donate some milk to your premature babies . . . and . . . just take a peep at Doran before I go. I'd really sleep much more comfortably.' How I blessed noting 'Daisy', the large mechanical breast pump gained my undying affection. The doctors invited me to follow them: I had won, and by the time I reached the clinic I was virtually a heroine. Human milk was in very short supply. I sat in the consulting room adjacent to where the cots and incubators stood. The nurses grew accustomed to me. Any cries of 'what's she doing here?' changed to 'bless her' once my purpose was disclosed.

Giving the milk helped me to feel part of the hospital. The effect was calming. I allowed myself to become fascinated by the curious pneumatic qualities of the pump. Finally, I delivered two brimming bottles to the fridge, carefully dated and labelled. The panic had left me. I asked to see Doran. It was now a foregone conclusion that I should. One of the nurses immediately began robing me in a white coat which fastened in the conventional way down the back and another pointed out the little side room which was used for phototherapy. This seemed to have the reverse effect of a sunray lamp – to bleach the skin.

'You'd better prepare yourself for how he's going to look,' she said. 'He won't be as you expect.'

'It doesn't really matter, does it?'

The little room was dark. In one corner stood a rectangular glass box, brilliantly lit up, and in the box lay the figure of Doran. He was naked except for the white nappy. His eyes were covered with two white pads, evidently to protect them from the light. There was a small shaved patch on his head where a wire had been inserted under the skin. His body was exquisitely proportioned. He looked so utterly perfect. For a moment, time stood still. I was hardly aware of what the nurse was telling me until she at last took my arm.

'We are giving him a drip,' she said, 'to stop him dehydrating. The hair will grow over quickly, don't worry.'

'I'm beyond worry,' I said, finding myself speaking half humorously, 'but I do want to do something. Can I feed him just a little?'

She looked perplexed.

'He's too weak now. He's been through quite a lot, you know.'

'Would you let me try tomorrow?'

She was still evidently perplexed by my suggestion.

'"They" don't usually suck well,' she said cautiously, 'but you can try.'

I could see Doran had already been diagnosed in her mind.

'I think Doran will be all right,' I said.

She looked at me with a mixture of pity and admiration.

'When shall I come?' I said.

She told me that the time for feeding the babies was six a.m.

'Will you still be here?'

'Yes, I go after the first feed so I'll see you then. Goodnight.'

'Goodnight.'

I carried the picture of Doran clearly in my mind. I was still very much awake; it was only the fifth day after his birth. The birth itself seemed far away; I felt closer to events still more distant and my mind moved from Doran to his father.

I was given night clothes and a sleeping pill and soon I lay in bed waiting for the night to disappear.

The events of my life made such a clear pattern that I knew I had all I needed to find my way through, if only I could use it properly. It was suddenly easy to talk to Peter again. I remembered how powerfully we had been drawn together; how death had haunted him and the forces of darkness taunted him until, finally, before he could destroy his love, he destroyed himself. How from that violence he had granted such an atmosphere of peace and love to our cottage that I came to understand and reach his spirit joyfully.

The absence of a body was almost unimportant. Talking to the dead became as easy and natural as smelling the flowers. Much of the time we'd spent affectionately laughing at each other. Then I knew he had settled me squarely in the world and he needed to move on . . .

But as I lay quietly, I could feel a warmth in my arms, and from far away through the great silence the knowledge became clear. Doran was now my guide. It was his road I was walking, and I would trust him.

2

***

I AWOKE with a clear and detailed awareness of all that had happened in the last twenty-four hours. It was a quarter to six. At six o'clock I was putting on the white coat which was my pass into the unit. This time I optimistically fastened the laces down the front and walked quickly between the cots to the darkened room with the light box and Doran. He appeared unchanged, neither asleep nor awake. The nurse looked up at me, she said, 'I'm afraid he'll be too sleepy to suck.'

'Why?'

'Well, he's been having a tranquillizer, phenobarbitone.'

'Why?'

'Well, it's usual,' she said. 'It stops them being so restless.'

'But surely he needs to be restless,' I said. 'Surely he needs stimulation?'

The nurse said she felt that two exchange transfusions were enough stimulation. I could see that outside Doran's room some of the babies were already in their nurses' arms and sucking bottles of milk.

'I'm sure I can make Doran suck,' I said stubbornly. 'Will you let me try?'

For answer she drew Doran out of the box and removed the patches from his eyes. Underneath them his eyes were open but remote. His body looked stiff, his hands were fisted; he made no response. I was willing him not to be dead. His ears were delicate and pointed; they looked as if they were intended to pick up the tiniest sound. I sat down in a chair by the box and the nurse extended Doran, wires and all, towards me very carefully, as if not to disturb his sleep. I undid my blouse and pressed him close to the familiar smell of my skin. Then I shook him a little, nothing happened; the drip looked pretty secure and I did not see how Doran could eat unless he woke up so I shook him a little harder and patted his cheeks as roughly as I dared. Then regardless of the apparent deafness I called his name. I only cared that he would drink. I demanded that he drank. The nurses were growing anxious and more eyes were gradually turning upon us. Doran's mouth came down suddenly in the right place, although still in a dream he began to make a slight sucking motion with his lips. It was at this moment that Doran's nurse came down squarely on my side.

'Could we try a bottle first?' she suggested. 'It may be easier for him.'

Doran's sucking increased in strength. Someone said, 'Look at that child suck, he's feeding better than some of the normal babies upstairs.'

It was the only normal thing Doran could do and he went on doing it.

The drip was discontinued. I had plenty of milk which I shared daily between Doran and Daisy and soon I was part of the landscape. No one questioned my movements, I could live as close to Doran as I pleased.

Catherine and Judy brought me food, clothes and drawing materials and, despite the hazardous predicament of Doran's body, we had a strange holiday of love. When I wasn't feeding Doran I could draw him; what I couldn't touch with my hand I could reach with my eyes. Fear of the future was temporarily suspended.

A week went by, after which the prognosis could not be postponed. When I had fed Doran, I was sent to my room to wait; the holiday was over and I must now face the facts. I could see how different Doran actually was from a normal baby but I loved him so much I could ignore it. My friends continued to behave as though he had a perfectly normal sort of a disease which time plus the right medical treatment could heal.

With the summons to go down, I passed from one world into another. I remember the corridor and the lift. Like the birth itself there was no way back; I must go on and on. In the lift I reached out for my angels, then composed and strangely relaxed I walked through the door of the familiar consulting room with Daisy in the corner. A group of medical staff stood next to the desk; as I moved towards them doctors and nurses seemed to melt away. I was left facing a small softly spoken man who seemed inwardly agonized by his duty.

'Mrs Scotson?'

'Yes,' I said. 'How do you do.'

He paid no real attention to my attempt to shake hands.

'I have bad news for you.'

He wanted to save me from illusions by coming straight to the point. The point was that there was rigidity in all Doran's limbs; his eyes, speech and hearing would, in all probability, be severely affected.

'His intelligence, however,' he continued as if in a desperate attempt to ameliorate the sentence, 'will probably not be harmed but' – he went on gently – 'it is perhaps the greatest of all the tragedies that he will never be able to use it.'

My instinct was to pick Doran up and run. His words came faster and faster. The doctors and nurses had slowly returned to the room and were all now giving me advice, as though Doran were no longer my child but a new kind of entity of which I could have no experience. Over and over again I heard the word 'they' used instead of 'he'. Doran now belonged to a kind of sub-species; he had lost his human identity. I looked towards the room where he lay. The pediatrician took hold of my shoulders, and sensing my disbelief he said, 'Do not look for a cure. It's impossible. There is none. Promise me you will not waste your time.'

I knew how I must appear to them – poor, recently bereaved and somewhat oddly dressed in an old Indian wrap around skirt and a faded blouse; but inside me love was powerful and I would not waste my time. I would do the impossible.

I felt almost caught in the morass of other people's fear, just as I had done after Peter died; and as I had fought then to stand by his dead body, now I fought again to reach Doran's broken, but still living one.

'I would like to go to him now,' I said. The crowd parted; I can't remember if they got me into a white coat. I only recall finding Doran lying in an ordinary crib and the astonishing relief of holding him in my arms. I wanted to give him some dignity, some privacy.

A disembodied voice interrupted us, 'We'll do what we can for you; I'm the hospital social worker. Are you sure you want to keep him?' I felt her leaning over me repeating the questions and I burst into tears; they washed over Doran closing out the meaning of the words.

For some time I spoke incoherently. I was full of anger and pain and love. Finally, my eyes were clear enough to look at the people who stood in a circle around us.

'You surely weren't expecting me to reject him,' I said. I was holding Doran as if I never intended to put him down again.

'Some mothers can't cope,' said the social worker. 'It's understandable.'

'Mrs Scotson,' said the pediatrician, 'you must understand that Doran will never fulfil his full potential.'

'Whatever happens,' I said half to myself, half to God, who couldn't avoid listening anyway, 'Doran will walk straight and tall and free. I swear it, I swear it.'

They let me take him up to my room. A cot was wheeled in but I kept him in my bed. It had been noted somewhere along the line that I had not actually taken any rest since Doran's birth and the staff nurse seized the opportunity of prescribing four days' enforced rest for both of us. I knew also they were giving me time to get used to Doran's condition. His body was stiff and his hands were fisted, he did not respond to light or sound, but he could feel my arms around him and my heart close to his. Over and over again I pressed out his fingers, and over and over again they curled defiantly back again.

Every four hours Doran was given three injections; there

was no doubt that he could feel them because he screamed loudly enough. I noticed that he always protested most loudly after the second injection as if to ward off the inevitability of a third. I thought he could count. I remembered a thousand years ago how his midwife had tried to protect him from a prick in the heel. They told me that the first two injections were antibiotic which was routine in his case, and the third was phenobarbitone. The antibiotic seemed inescapable but I protested against the continued use of phenobarbitone. Doran had little enough sensory information and to artificially dull the remainder must be unreasonable. The staff nurse was Irish and very sympathetic; she decided to 'have a word with the doctors'.

'He's a lot more peaceful now he's with you,' she said. 'Do you think he can hear?' I shook my head. It was hard to admit but Doran didn't tremble at the little noises that cause ordinary babies to shoot their arms in the air. You could explode a kiss in his ear and he would remain less affected than a china doll.

'Not yet,' I said.

'Well, let's try a little harder,' she said.

She produced a large brass bell, like the bell they used to ring in the school yard and shook it vigorously above his head. She was loathe to give up, but every other baby in the ward was awake and crying while Doran stared obliviously into space. There was no need to go far to compare the difference between him and other babies. I could watch other babies being wheeled endlessly back and forth from the maternity ward to the nursery; these children were open to the world, their movements were varied and vital, their responses eloquent, their sleep relaxed and peaceful; it was true that Doran did not belong with them, his body shut the world firmly out.

I remembered how much pleasure I took in music and in the endless sounds of wind and the sounds of the birds in the eaves of our cottage. It was autumn now and you felt you could hear the leaves talking and the children biting into apples . . . I remembered how as a child I was comforted by the little familiar sounds about the house which took my loneliness away

23

and let me sleep. If Doran was irretrievably deaf it would be just one of many disabilities and his other senses would be unlikely to sharpen to compensate, so I had to believe that Doran was not irretrievably deaf. It was a very unreasonable belief on the evidence, but I preferred to be unreasonable.

The Irish nurse remained unreasonable too. She went on trying to find some sound to which Doran would react, while I imagined myself in a silent world. Sound became painful to me because I knew that Doran was deprived of it.

At last they decided to discharge us mid-morning. Doran was dressed and our things packed together. Catherine had been recalled to work three days ago and as I knew no one who was free at that time, a hospital car was the solution to our homecoming. Without phenobarbitone Doran was able to express himself and it was clear that he and I would need a night at home to work out our relationship before Lili joined us. Doran was evidently very terrified and very very angry; he fought his terror every inch of the way. He was still strong and very good at throwing his head back violently, arching his spine and screaming. A way to reduce this protest was to put him over my knee or across my shoulder and thump him hard on the back. If this failed, the technique could be supplemented by my dancing round and round with him; but when I actually tried throwing him up in the air the protest began again.

Catherine and Judy had left the cottage looking very pretty. They had even gone so far as to decorate the cot in the spare room as a delicate suggestion that I might leave Doran there to sleep. Doran, however, was communicating very clearly that he would not sleep wherever I put him down, at any time, or in any place. In short, I would be ill-advised to put him down. I was at home and not at home. We couldn't share what we saw or heard because Doran couldn't see or hear; we couldn't share rest because Doran couldn't tire himself. Some pattern had to be established, but how? I paced between the kitchen and the living room, then I tried walking up and down the stairs thumping Doran's back and trying to imagine a plausible future. I ate my lunch while still pacing the floor.

Intermittently I fed Doran. His eating was always desperate. He sucked too fast, developed violent indigestion and then sought refuge in more food. I tried him in the baby sling but the complaints he made at my efforts to get him into it should have warned me of his verdict.

Later that afternoon our midwife arrived; she was, in a sense, the first of a long line of people whose experience of brain injury and its consequences on a family meant a continuous struggle to keep parents in the no-man's-land between despair and hope. She agreed that Doran seemed to be deaf and while I continued to calm her small patient by patting his back with considerable firmness, I wondered if I could persuade her to agree with a more optimistic explanation I'd been developing in my own mind.

'His screams are so loud it's hard to believe he doesn't know I can hear them,' I said. 'Do you think it's possible his hearing could be merely traumatized so that he could only hear his own screams?'

She would obviously like to have said yes, but her training prevented her. She told me gently, repeating herself to make sure I understood, that once the auditory nerve was destroyed, that was it. Finish – the hearing could not return. Then she still more gently suggested asking a teacher of the deaf to come and visit me each week and help prepare me for life with a deaf child. I could do no more than agree. As she left my doctor called, so I tried another approach.

'Of course,' I said, 'they couldn't be absolutely sure about it at the hospital, but they did say his injury was likely to be severe; and I think they are correct – Doran looks like a severely brain injured child. Do you agree?'

He was relieved. He did agree and was glad to see how well I was taking it.

'Just take each day as it comes,' he said. 'He's only a baby.'

I said, 'Won't he be a man one day?'

'You mustn't worry about the future,' he said. 'Remember great happiness can come out of great sorrow.'

I was genuinely sorry for him. What could he say? My

situation was absurd. The next morning after a little sleep and a great deal of thumping and dancing with Doran as my director, I found a new face in my house, a health visitor. She was followed quickly by the social worker. There was nothing they could do beyond confirm facts; I felt they still had a suspicion that Doran would be better off in an institution. I didn't want to hear any more negative things about Doran; I longed for some positive help to get him well.

By lunch time we had been collected and driven to pick up Lili by 'Bert', a woman friend of exactly the blend of affection and practicality I needed. She held Doran and thumped him in the way he liked while I waited for Lili to finish her lunch.

'Mummy,' she said, setting her eyes on me at last and patting the arm of her friend, 'this is Lucy.' At that time she looked well and confident although her host pointed out that all the children had slight colds.

So Lili came home; we were united and we had a party. Bert stayed on thumping Doran while I read Lili a story and tucked her in her own bed.

I had another stimulating night with Doran before me. I realized night and day were to become much the same to both of us. For the next few days the weather was good and Lili, having no other experience of a brother, was undaunted by his behaviour. We spent our time on tour around the gardens of those friends who could produce troupes of children whose company Lili could enjoy, and whose shouting drowned Doran's characteristic protestation. It was an Indian summer, but the sunshine seemed far away and Lili's cold grew gradually worse.

I took her to the doctor. He agreed that she had a cold, but colds weren't unusual and one got over them. Lili, however, did not seem to be getting over this cold. She couldn't sleep. She could hear that I was up with Doran and before long she was up too. Now I was dancing with both children in my arms.

The Indian summer blew back to India taking its magic colours and leaving the air nostalgically chilly. Lili's cold persisted, and Doran grew more fierce in his demands to gain some contact with the world. I had learned to manage every possible domestic necessity without putting him down. This included lifting Lili in and out of the kitchen sink, the one place where she was warm, happy, safe and tidy for an indefinite period of time. It was hard to light a fire holding one child and reading a story to another, but not impossible.

Once upon a time, I had planned a flamboyant and fashionable career in the arts for the three of us; since God had taken some pains to change our direction, I presumed he meant to keep us alive. This was a preserving thought because Lili was now drowning in her own catarrh. She had begun to cough; it was a ferocious choking as if she were fighting off a wild animal. In the midst of everything Doran had a check up at the hospital which meant a further cataloguing of his various disabilities. At that time he hated having his clothes removed, especially his nappy. Nevertheless, he was formally stripped. As the doctor bent over him, Doran peed straight into his eye – a reflex action no doubt, but a bold one. The affronted medic wiped his face and paused to listen to Lili coughing.

'That child,' he said, 'has whooping cough. You're in for a difficult time with her.'

I now had two sick children. I drove home to the accompaniment of screaming and coughing and my reflections that I had no money to cushion any further trouble should it arise.

The best solution was the only solution. As soon as I arrived at the cottage I phoned my parents. They lived a long way away and were neither young nor fit, but they both had stores of youthfulness for emergencies and this was by definition an emergency. My mother came by train and collected Lili from the station. My two-year-old daughter looked more like an old woman. She was bent to brace herself against another fit of coughing; her face was grey and drawn. She left without tears; she was too ill to do anything but trust.

A week passed, and then another. We met the teacher for the deaf who told us about grammar schools for the deaf and careers for the deaf, such as truck driving. She didn't realize the extent of Doran's injuries and I couldn't bear to tell her

27

because I liked hearing this unusually positive talk.

One night after she had left, I was aware that Doran had actually fallen asleep in my arms. I carried him upstairs and laid him in my bed and there he was still asleep. I was almost stunned by the sudden liberty of being able to execute an infinite number of domestic tasks with two hands. An hour went by; it was almost a strain expecting to be recalled from the kitchen sink. I squeezed out the clothes I was washing, dried my hands and decided to sleep as well.

Doran was undisturbed but he was different. I had plenty of time to study him, his developmental changes were minute or non-existent; they needed the eyes of an enthusiast to record. At this moment I felt sure he looked more relaxed, as if some of the harmony from his surroundings had flowed into him. I held my breath and slammed the door. I saw Doran catch his breath; the pause was slight but to me so momentous I was hardly breathing myself. He could hear.

I climbed into bed and encircled him with my arms. His cheek was soft next to mine and I began to stroke his forehead gently. Then I became aware of a colourless liquid flowing steadily from his left ear. As I was wondering how to bear this new complication I noticed that my own cheeks were wet; his whole face was wet from my tears.

3

---❋---

BY MORNING Doran produced the most animated sound I had yet heard from him; he sneezed. The sneezing developed into a full blown cold. I remembered that Lili's cold had developed into whooping cough and thought it was worth seeing my doctor immediately. Dr — was quite confident that breast fed babies, brain injured or otherwise, didn't catch whooping cough.

The next day, I had been invited to a healing service. I persuaded myself that if I took enough paper handkerchiefs and kept Doran well wrapped up in my coat it would prevent him passing any further infirmity onto the congregation. I had no memory of being particularly at ease in a church; nevertheless it seemed unusually important that Doran and I did go.

We arrived just in time. There was another woman at my elbow holding a little girl. She had bright eyes and fair hair and a very tiny body. Someone had passed me a prayer sheet and as I looked up the singing began. Love swept through me and my eyes streamed with tears. I had to bite my fist to prevent my drowning the service by actually howling. Doran was totally absorbed in food, and not sneezing, which was good because I needed all his handkerchiefs. Somehow I was directed towards the altar for the laying on of hands. I was light-headed and still crying when the congregation trouped out.

We remained for five or six minutes. There was an unusual serenity until I started to cough. Someone found me a glass of water. I could only communicate in smiles and gestures. My best refuge was the car. Doran lay quietly in his carrycot all the way home.

I could hear the phone ringing as we opened the gate. I picked up the receiver, my coughing cascaded into the mouthpiece. Judy was speaking.

'So how's Doran?'

'Better,' I managed to say.

'You sound worse.'

I couldn't argue.

'Linda, you should put Doran down. All babies cry, it's a reflex.'

'Thanks for the advice.'

'I know you're not going to take it,' she said.

My cough developed with much more style than Doran's cold. I became the helpless occupant of a body through which a kind of hurricane shuddered at frequent intervals. At least, I thought, to look on the bright side, with Doran's new hearing he can't mistake his mother. I made another appointment with my doctor at the earliest opportunity which was nearly a week away.

It was impossible to rest lying down. On the other hand, if I had the good fortune to fall asleep in an upright position I immediately fell sideways and woke up. Doran struggled for his food several times during the night and this, combined with the still frequent dance intervals, kept us entertained until morning.

But by the morning I was due to go to the doctor's, I knew I was not going to be able to get up. Any change in my position produced a raging storm in my lungs. I dialled the doctor who pointed out that he was very busy and unable to see me until the evening calls. I dialled my health visitor who was sympathetic but busy. I dialled Judy who was at work.

'I'm finally losing my sense of humour,' I said.

Judy was a forthright American, she said, 'You're going to hospital.'

'How?'

She hung up.

Just after one o'clock the front door banged. Someone was in the house. I felt that if the burglar could change a nappy and perhaps bring me a cup of tea he was welcome.

Footsteps began heading lightly upstairs.

A few moments later the intruder was using my phone. 'Queen Victoria Hospital, its Dr —. Can you admit a mother and baby. The mother has suspected pneumonia.'

Very soon I was lying in a white room having my limbs washed and watching Doran curled in the arms of an adoring nurse. The ward liked babies and even a rather wrecked baby like Doran was evidently sheer bliss. Despite his inability to hold up his head and the way his eyes persisted in setting like half moons just above the bridge of his nose, Doran was a handsome figure. He knew he was appreciated because instead of screaming he audibly purred.

He had a line of nurses eager to change him, cuddle him and otherwise delight in him. I had never seen him happy before; I had never been able to forget the worry about him and sleep, but now I slept. When I stopped sleeping I had visitors. I requested a copy of *The Tibetan Book of the Dead* and my drawing materials. I drew Doran and dreamed of Tibetan lamas. This delightful state of affairs continued until Doran made a new impression on the ward; there was no escaping the fact that he was whooping.

After some debate it was decided to send both of us as patients to the children's wing of another hospital which was equipped with oxygen masks. Directly after lunch we were packed and ready to go. From the ambulance windows the familiar countryside looked curious and far away, an unapproachable looking-glass world.

We arrived at a low bunker-like building in the hospital grounds. Hands reached in for Doran and hurried him peremptorily to one of several large rooms. Two-thirds of the walls were glass, the remainder was painted green, the floor looked blue. The tube lighting overhead hummed as it was turned up; it would adequately have sickened the rosiest of complexions. (Later I discovered that although it could be turned down it couldn't actually be turned off.) There were two iron cots in the room and a very high iron bed. From these the paint was either flaking with age or had been assiduously kicked in desperate struggles of long ago. Doran was taken to the smaller of the cots which closely resembled a cage. He recommenced screaming and when the side of the cage was unlocked and the nursing sister thrust him in, his protestation grew louder and more intense. The room was relatively cold; without a word she began to strip off his smart red stretch suit, then she departed remarking on the necessity of his having hospital clothing. I wrapped him up in my coat and waited. She returned bearing the only item resembling a stretch suit she could find. It was thin and torn and had broken press studs, besides which it did not fit. Gratefully I replaced Doran's own clothes and before she could close down the cot sides I scooped him out.

'He's not going to like that,' I said firmly.

'But you can't possibly hold him.'

'I can,' I said. 'Doran needs to be held, and if necessary I shall hold him all the time.'

'As you wish,' she said and left.

There was one straight backed chair and the very high bed to choose from as alternatives to standing. I tried the bed and discovered it had a plastic undersheet and paper pillow slips, over very slippery plastic covered pillows. After pacing about the room in considerable discomfort I noticed that the chair close to the door was suddenly occupied by 'lunch', a paper plate of rather watery baked beans which was difficult to hold without it bending. Cups of tea were available in a room down the corridor. I decided to rest my hopes on tea, and Doran and I commenced an excursion in that direction. We were instantly surrounded by three nurses and pressed back to a chorus of, 'The baby is in isolation! You cannot take him out! Leave him in his cot.' My attention was drawn to the sign on our glass door. It read, 'Full Barrier Nursing'. I began to grasp its meaning.

I discovered that two toilets existed and they were both far away down another winding corridor at the opposite end of the building. Contact with the staff consisted of the intermittent arrival of antibiotics in miniature milkshake glasses. The nurses wore Mickey Mouse pinafores over their uniforms and moved by so quickly that it was the memory of Mickey Mouse and not an individual face that left an impression. The only hope of my passage to the loo was to put Doran into the arms of the nurse who came with the antibiotic. But the milkshake glasses seemed to arrive with such sleight of hand that the nurse who brought them was often far away before I could make any request.

Doran hated his antibiotic. Inducing him to swallow it involved the one part of his body over which he had some control. He could regurgitate perfectly and to order. The moment after I believed I had been successful in pouring the sticky liquid down his throat it reappeared on the floor. The antibiotic seemed to be a routine measure and I privately felt that he knew he was being offered too much.

In contrast to his size and condition Doran always gave me the impression I was with someone very strong. I could never be described as being alone with a baby when I was in fact in the company of a forceful and fascinating friend.

We spent as little time as possible on the high slithery bed which was the most dangerous place in the room for the act of sleep. No one came to clean the room, so as far as possible, I did it myself, enhancing our reputation for eccentricity by singing and miming to every fragment of a song I could remember. One evening I felt hot and dirty enough to merit a bath and when Doran decided to take one of his infrequent naps I decided to improvise at the washbasin. The clean hot water felt superb. I had the plan to wash and dry myself in sections, using the towels to divide up the sections, but, before I could progress very far, the door burst open and a group of nurses rushed in pushing a screen and protesting wildly. I had evidently forgotten about the glass windows in my walls. It was true; having spent days unsuccessfully trying to catch someone's eye to ask them for help, I had begun to assume the glass was not very transparent.

33

I was now in trouble. Doran had woken up and was whooping and the bath was at an end. I dressed quickly and was standing with Doran in my arms when the nursing sister arrived.

'Mrs Scotson, we are trying to treat this child for whooping cough and you are making it very difficult.'

'I'm sorry,' I said, 'but I'm treating him for brain injury and *you* are making it very difficult.'

Then without a clear understanding of my intention, I brushed past her and carried Doran all the way down the corridor to the physicians' office. There were three men sitting round a longish table drinking tea.

'I'm discharging us both,' I said. 'I shall explain why. I should like to phone for a taxi as soon as possible.'

Eyebrows rose. I was suddenly very angry and very clear and the three men had their explanation of this expostulation there and then.

It produced remarkable consequences. With almost deferential politeness we were offered an ambulance to take us straight back to the Queen Victoria Hospital. No further questions were to be asked.

We arrived back to find a welcoming party at the door. The loving hands we had previously left swept around us. We were destined to be spoilt continuously, and by everyone.

The night before we left was very still. Doran woke me from time to time sucking in his sleep. My cheek felt comfortably cradled against the pillow. My body was stretched out and at ease and I began thinking how lucky I was for this moment of safety. This train of thought was interrupted by the sound of someone struggling to clear their throat. The struggle was still going on when I eventually fell asleep. Early next morning as I was tiptoeing back from the lavatory, a long metal box glided past me. My instinct was to connect it with lunch, which usually arrived in tubs set into a similarly large steel container to preserve their warmth. Then I noticed that the lid was smooth and that it was gliding away from an empty bed. The screens had been drawn back and the equipment that had once been secluded behind them now followed in procession behind the box. Nothing was said. By 12 o'clock there were two newly vacated beds, and Doran and I had our coats on and were ready to go home.

We had been away three weeks. In two more, Lili would join us. The house was in a similar state of chaos to the scene of our departure, except for a certain overripeness of a pan of soup and a few vegetables. Doran was quite happy to be swept from one shoulder to another while I worked. He expected to be treated as respectfully as any other part of my body.

It was five o'clock and almost dark when the taxi arrived. My mother came in carrying an enormous bundle of blankets. When the bundle was safe beside me on the sofa it disclosed an eye; the eye looked at me and closed and then as the blankets shifted slightly I saw both eyes open.

'It's me,' I said.

'I know, mummy,' Lili smiled, yawned, and went on sleeping.

Somehow my mother, Lili, Doran and I all slept together in the same bed. The next morning at Lili's request she had a bath with Doran. To hold my son in any position which didn't involve his head shooting under the water or me climbing into the bath too, was a considerable athletic feat. In the midst of a steamy, water swamped bathroom it was just possible to catch enough sight of Doran's face to see he was smiling.

When we drove back from taking my mother to the station, the December sun shone and Lili was being sufficiently boisterous with Doran in his carrycot for him to feel secure. I stopped at the village shop and was caught coming out, smiling and swathed in children, by an old acquaintance.

'You're all home,' she exclaimed. 'How wonderful! I must rush, but,' she added as she turned to slam her car door, 'nothing more can happen to you now!'

'That's tempting fate,' I said, and laughed.

Doran was still very evidently brain injured and I was still as dedicated to find a way out for him. We went on to a children's party where the change in Doran's confidence was very evident; he allowed himself to be dragged about the floor and passed between Lili's friends like the favourite rag doll. Lili had clearly regained her appetite but Doran was disinterested in food. I admired his new independence and was sorry when I had to interfere to change a series of very dirty nappies. I thought something I had eaten had affected my milk and given him an upset stomach. By the time we left, the intensity of the mess seemed to have decreased and it seemed foolish to worry.

That night while Lili slept I changed Doran once, twice, three times. By the fourth time I could put up a reasonable case that something *more* had happened to us. By now the nappies were full of a kind of dry grit which the cramp in his stomach blasted into them with discomforting force. I could connect the dry grit with the failure to drink, and the failure to drink was a memorable feature of the past. It was a quarter to midnight when I phoned my doctor. He was not altogether happy to turn out. I seemed to mean continuous trouble and the end of his peaceful life.

By half past twelve he was examining Doran in the kitchen. Almost the total number of Doran's clothes were soaking in the kitchen sink and Doran himself became a sickly green colour. He wasn't crying; he was totally exhausted by the uncontrollable muscular spasms. The doctor felt his head.

'Well, he's not dehydrated.'

'But what's the matter?'

'I think he's got a touch of the old gastro.'

'You mean gastroenteritis.'

I knew it was fatal in budgerigars and always serious in infants.

'Doesn't that mean hospital again?' I asked, almost longing to be back in the safety of the Queen Vic.

'Steady on,' he said, 'if the little chap takes some milk during the night, he should be okay, Linda.'

'Do you really think so?'

'Give me a ring in the morning if you have any problems,' he said and made his way out, back to the safety of his own bed.

Doran did take a little milk during the night but it was only a little. The gritty diarrhoea continued but the nappies were always dry; there was no pee left in Doran. It was Saturday and Judy and Bert arrived. They settled down to read stories to Lili while I wrestled to persuade my son to suck. His eyes began to move restlessly from side to side. I saw the fear in him I'd known before and this time it was critical that I act in time.

I tried to dial the practice; again and again I was getting 'number unobtainable'. I had an old fashioned telephone with the letters of the alphabet grouped alongside the numbers. I realized that I was dialling my doctor's name. When I could control myself enough to get through, the receptionist said, 'I'm sorry, Dr — is out.' She paused and went on, 'Would you like a colleague?'

'Yes, yes please. It's urgent – anything.'

Someone was put on the line. I was prepared to say anything to get Doran to hospital but before I had stumbled over the first words he was telling me crisply, 'Yes, I think you should go immediately. An ambulance will be on the way in about half an hour.'

'Which hospital?'

'Brighton. They have a kidney unit,' he said. 'Good luck.'

I put the phone down in ecstasy of relief.

'How long?' asked Bert.

'Half an hour,' I said. 'I think he'll survive that.'

'Half an hour,' said Judy, 'is great. You can pack.'

My first thought was food rather than clothes. I swept the contents of the fridge into carrier bags. Meanwhile Judy and Bert had found a suitcase and were deciding what the three of us would need and for how long.

The sound of a heavy vehicle backing down the lane prevented further speculation. Judy slammed the lid of the case. 'That's it,' she said. Bert opened the door and two ambulance men backed in carrying a stretcher.

'He's a bit small for that,' she said. The ambulance men looked a little crestfallen so we put Lili on the stretcher. The

37

luggage was tucked away and before my friends could finish their affectionate lectures on how to look after myself, the ambulance door was shut and we were off.

Doran's dry lips still pulled gently against me but the effort of swallowing was too much for him.

'Mummy, am I ill?' Lili asked from the stretcher.

'You're only pretend ill this time, darling.'

'Is it Doran then?'

'It does seem to be Doran again, Lili.'

The hospital staff were quick and gentle. Doran's head was shaved and he was given another saline drip. He was awake but passive.

'He's a good baby,' said the nurse as she strapped the tube to his head. 'Has he got something the matter with his eyes?'

I realized that they had no notes on his medical history.

'He's been through a lot already,' I said. 'He's a survivor.'

The room was white, there were pictures on the walls and toys on the shelves; a low freshly turned down bed fitted under the window. Lili settled onto the bed and a wall of medical staff closed around Doran. I stood quietly listening. One of the doctors turned to me, 'It's an unusual case and I don't think we can handle it here. Our best bet is to try to get you up to Guy's.'

'Please explain.'

'Willingly.'

The man had a quiet Lancastrian accent and a deliberate way of speaking that made you feel he believed you were alive. Doran had succumbed to a kidney virus to which most children were immune. His condition was known as the 'haemolytic uraemic syndrome, which meant that he was in danger of dying from either dehydration or anaemia. He needed a blood transfusion but this could not be contemplated before he was rehydrated. Rehydration was a delicate matter because there was risk of over-hydration which was also dangerous. Then there was the question of resting his kidneys until they recovered, which meant getting him to a kidney machine as soon as possible.

38

I knew kidney machines were like gold dust and it occurred very strongly to me that many people would think this virus was a suitable exit from a life of dependence and handicap.

'I've put a call through to Guys',' said the doctor. 'Can you tell me anything else about him meanwhile?' He nodded towards the group of white-coated figures surrounding Doran.

'He's very strong,' I said, 'and he does mean to live and he's brave and . . .' All I could feel was a rising terror that somehow Peter's son would slip through my fingers. I recounted his background slowly and desperately, emphasizing Doran's intelligence and trying to use the word 'traumatization', which sounded more temporary, instead of 'brain injury'.

The phone rang. The doctor excused himself and then coming back said, 'Well, we are going to "traumatize" him again. They think we can cope tonight and there will be a machine ready for him at Guy's tomorrow morning. You're in luck.'

They hovered over Doran for the rest of the day. Lili elected to sleep in the bed with the toys. She said she wanted to keep an eye on Doran. I was given a small room next door and told the value of sleep. Nevertheless sleep was an unnatural pastime and when I had let what I considered to be a polite length of time elapse, I got up and returned to his room. The atmosphere was charged. I did not know why. The nurses were too worried themselves to remember I was supposed to be sleeping. Every so often Doran's eyelids flickered and a tremor ran through his body. I watched one of the nurses time these events. Finally, I asked, 'What's happening to him?'

'He's been fitting,' she said, and then raising her eyes to her colleague, 'I think we should call the doctor.' She left immediately. The other nurse bent over Doran. He was a baby with a history – the marks of two bald patches on his head, drips, drugs, whooping cough, kidney failure. Doran began to have another seizure.

'Can you stop it?' I asked.

'There are anti-convulsants,' she replied. 'We'll see what the doctors recommend.'

'Will it have an effect on him – I mean in the long term?'

'He's been very ill, hasn't he?'

'Yes, but this fitting, could *this* fitting by itself do any permanent damage?'

'It is possible,' she paused; 'but they are often very happy children you know, and he's lucky to have such a loving mother. Intelligence isn't everything.'

She adjusted the drip. I looked towards the window and imagined the sky being blue.

4

THE NURSE stopped talking, she was watching for another seizure. For a few seconds Doran's eyes moved rapidly under their lids; she wrote down the time and the duration of the event.

I said, 'Was that a seizure?' She nodded. 'Could that really damage him much?' 'Yes,' she said, 'it's possible.'

'I can't believe it.'

The room seemed to be growing smaller. I was curling and uncurling my toes in my shoes. Two of Doran's doctors came in followed by his nurse. They examined their patient and flicked through the notes. The second doctor, an Australian, remarked, 'I see he's had a few more convulsions; but we can expect that.'

His companion met my eyes, 'He'll be all right at Guy's. They've got all the big stuff up there.'

'But what about the convulsions he's having now? I'm used to the idea of convulsions meaning brain injury.'

The Australian shook his head, 'In his case they're just a warning that his kidneys are packing in. Don't worry, you're in time. And you've got a tough kid over there.'

I was suddenly blissfully tired. I caught myself yawning. I said, 'Are you really sure about those convulsions?'

'I'm over ninety-eight per cent sure.'

'Doran's my son,' I said, 'but he's more than that; he's an old friend. He keeps teaching me things and I keep learning. It's an interesting arrangement.'

He put a hand on my shoulder, 'Then as his friend I advise you to get some more sleep. It's a big day tomorrow; he'll be needing you.'

41

I said, 'Since you're a man who's ninety-eight per cent sure I'll take your advice.'

That night my pillow was soft. Although the hospital morning began well ahead of the sun there was something of the refreshing excitement of sunrise in me. I had slept well. Doran had survived the latter part of the night successfully and he now had the prospect of travelling with a doctor and nurse as well as a police escort, ahead of him. It was evidently a big event to send a patient up to Guy's.

Lili was invited to the nurses' kitchen for breakfast. She chose malt bread, banana and peanut butter; the meal gave the occasion an almost festive air. At last we emerged from the ward and proceeded towards the ambulance. The doctor carried Doran; the nurse held the drip to which he was still very much attached; Lili embraced a large teddy bear, loaned for the trip; and I took our suitcase and the remains of my larder still in a large plastic bag.

The police escort arrived and we settled ourselves on the rather high slippery seats of the ambulance. Most of the journey was an exercise in keeping the drip stable – ambulances have no noticeable springs – and keeping up a lively speculation as to what might happen next. Somewhere in the back of my mind I was aware that technically Doran was hovering between life and death. What was unusual was that he did not have an aura of weakness about him.

Guy's tower block was enormously high, bright and imposing. It had its own magic. We were escorted out on to its gleaming floors, engulfed by medical stuff, whisked into a lift and precipitated upwards to the kidney ward. The new white walls swept past as we turned briskly down the main corridor. Sheets of white paper had been glued up and teams of small children were busily engaged in making some continuous and dramatic painting. Further on we ploughed through piles of gold and silver tinsel and mounds of coloured paper. 'Is this normal?' I asked.

'It's Christmas,' someone charitably replied.

We poured into a small room filled with gleaming, impressive equipment. Doran was stripped and laid in an open incubator. Nothing was demanded of Lili or myself, so we sat silently on a chair by the window, watching a very small body joined to a very large network of life support systems.

The conversation was quite open and I could hear clearly how dangerous the next few weeks were going to be. The immediate worries were rehydration and the blood transfusion. It was also vital to keep a balance between the sodium and potassium in Doran's blood, sodium and potassium were known as electrolytes, and cases like Doran's were renowned for their constant crises. Frequent adjustments to the electrolytes had to be made. Again and again a decision would be taken which would risk Doran's life.

The consultant quietly evaluated the opinions of his colleagues. There was an honest, direct way in which they discussed the risks and the degree of human error under which they worked. I saw that they were used to fighting; Doran already belonged to them.

At last the group seemed temporarily satisfied. They all smiled, relieved to have come so far; Doran could have his blood transfusion. There was a general feeling that although I could be with him as much as I wished, I ought to go and have a cup of tea. I decided it was good manners to trust that they could keep Doran alive for ten minutes without me. The room was full to bursting but as I stood up to go, Lili pulled my sleeve. 'Doran will be lonely.'

'Doran is extraordinarily good at making friends.'

She said, 'I'll get him a doll.' Then she hammered on his incubator, 'Bye bye, Doran, we'll come back soon.'

Lili had a sixth sense about dolls. She knew they lived in the playroom where the tea-vending machine stood and where the children who were fit enough to walk about, ate their meals. While the nurse gave me gentle directions, she was off running ahead down the corridor. Every child I passed seemed aware of where I was going and was more than willing to lead me there.

Lili decided that the jumble of dolls in the playroom needed a party. She was soon joined by a group of young patients: the kidney ward had already accepted her as part of their world. I was sitting on a small chair surrounded by children when the play leader appeared. 'Take your tea,' she said. 'They want you in the consultant's office. I'll look after Lili.'

I walked across the corridor feeling already reasonably confident. The office door was flanked by the epic adventures of Cinderella and wreathed in tinsel. The room was decorated with comforting winter scenes by Pieter Breugel. Doran's consultant and the registrar sat at a desk in front of me.

The facts about Doran were very clear; recovery would be long and difficult – a month at the shortest, maybe three months. At any moment the condition could deteriorate for a variety of causes. The staff were on a minute by minute alert. He would have a nurse in constant attendance day and night. His pulse, his heart, his temperature, his weight, his fluid balance, his blood pressure had to be monitored every half hour. I could be with him all the time. There was a room available along his corridor. 'And Lili?' I asked. 'Naturally she will be with me.'

The men looked uncomfortable. I realized that I had taken it for granted that Lili could stay. They explained that it was not Guy's policy to accommodate other children in the family. Besides Lili had a nasty chest infection which might communicate itself to other patients. They were kind but extremely firm. Lili must go as soon as possible. They understood my hesitation but hadn't I friends in London? I had hardly understood that outside Guy's hospital there was a city called London.

London had baptized me in my student days. It had brought me up; it had led me into temptation and delivered me from evil; but most of all it had given me friends. I had more friends in London than the rest of the world put together. I remember the nearest table I had danced on. It belonged to Peter and Theresa Marinker and their children, Eicher and Daniel. Daniel had been born a year before Doran on the same date.

If the family were at home, I knew instinctively someone

44

would come. I took my purse from Doran's room and went to the pay phone by the desk in the main corridor. In a few words it was confirmed that Theresa would collect Lili. The next thing was to tell Lili. She was still involved with her tea party. I found her sitting amongst a row of happy dolls; she pressed a tea cup and an imaginary biscuit into my hand. Perhaps it would be better not to tell her? Then it struck me that if I was clutching a tea cup in one hand and an imaginary biscuit in the other, I didn't have my purse. I excused myself and ran back to the telephone. The purse was there, but like the proverbial ghost ship, it was empty. Money somehow was not a very serious thing to lose. I hoped whoever took it needed it.

Lili was coming down the corridor to look for me. 'Let's go and see Doran,' I said, and together we crept into his room and sat on the floor. The transfusion was very slow, a doctor and nurse were always there, sometimes two doctors, sometimes a whole team. We watched Doran appear and disappear behind these figures. Lili became hungry so I unpacked some biscuits and cheese and a knife and began to share a meal with her. 'Will Doran be here at Christmas?' she asked.

'I expect so, do you want to be here at Christmas?'

'I want to be with Doran.'

There was a knock at the door. A nurse popped her head in. 'You have a visitor,' she said. We scrambled up. Theresa was outside. She hugged Lili. 'Lili, darling, are you going to come home with me and see Daniel?' Lili smiled, 'Is mummy coming too?' I said, 'Lili, we both have to be very brave because I have to stay here.'

Theresa picked Lili up and cuddled her, we walked out of the ward to the car park: 'Being brave is an adventure, Lili,' I said, 'but it's hard work too.'

'Is Doran working hard, mummy?'

'Very hard, Lili, so that he can get well and be with you again.'

Theresa was worried about the traffic, so we kissed and separated.

I paused and then feeling the cold suddenly, I ran back into

45

the building. I was aware of being distinctly uncomfortable across my chest. The milk that Doran hadn't been drinking was building up. I was glad to be back in his room. I sat still, simply keeping in touch with his life. The medical staff continued coming and going, but after a while they were reduced to a Yorkshire doctor and a Canadian nurse.

'He's no trouble,' the nurse said. 'It's unusual.' The doctor turned to me, talking as if we were recommencing a conversation. 'He's very helpful, your lad.'

I said, 'It's the least he can be since you're going to so much trouble.' 'Trouble,' he said. 'It has been trouble, but I think we've got a good start now.'

'Good enough to ask when I can feed him again? I've got an unlimited supply of milk.'

'As things are,' he said, 'I'd hold on to that for a bit.'

The door opened and the registrar entered with a cup of black tea. 'If you were looking for milk,' his colleague remarked, 'she's got it.'

'Milk,' said the registrar. 'If she's found the milk she's cleverer than I am.'

'I didn't have to look for it,' I said. 'I'm overloaded.'

'She means mother's milk,' said the Yorkshire doctor. 'It's really Doran's milk,' I said, 'and I want to donate it to your wonderful hospital while I'm waiting to feed him.' 'Thanks,' said the registrar, 'but I'd better send you to special care. They'll welcome you with open arms.'

'Then I'll go now,' I said. 'Stay with him.'

'Like leeches,' they assured me.

I ran to the lift. Running was the normal way of getting about the hospital, and I wanted to give the milk in the minimum amount of time.

The special care baby unit presented me with a bottle and a hissing machine which drew off what looked like nearly a third of a pint of milk. My body seemed to produce milk in generous quantities regardless of my stress. The donation was received with great enthusiasm and I promised to return three times a day.

I spent most of the night with Doran; so did the medical team. When I did lie down a sudden absolute tiredness gave me two hours' deep rest which was more refreshing than anyone could expect. By morning Doran was just winding up the transfusion; surviving the night was a victory and everyone seemed very positive. In Doran's situation survival was a continuous cause for celebration. The watchword for the team was 'staying power'; they were constantly on call. My next duty was to go and donate the milk.

I was hurrying back along the corridor when I encountered the registrar apparently running to meet me and evidently very pleased about something.

'Congratulations!' he cried. 'Your daughter's just been admitted. It's a great privilege; she's in the next ward. Now you can just breeze between the two.'

I wondered if I was the first person in the world to be congratulated for having a child admitted to hospital. I stared at him. 'We've admitted her as a suspected pneumonia,' he beamed. 'Now you can have your entire family with you for Christmas.' He took my arm and steered me through some glass doors into another ward. Lili was sitting on a bed coughing and spluttering and nose streaming. Peter and Theresa were both with her.

'It's wonderful,' I said to everyone at once. 'She can stay!' Peter suddenly pressed some money into my hand. 'You'll need it,' he said, 'because we won't be able to see you for a while. We're all going to Cambridge for Christmas.'

So Lili had a room which was bright and pretty, and collected increasing numbers of cuddly toys. I made sure I was with her as she went to sleep and before she woke up; for the rest of the day I took the registrar's advice and simply 'breezed' between the two. If Doran was a little indifferent to visitors, Lili was not. I phoned up everyone I could think of and told them we'd come home, under Doran's direction, to the big city.

When the initial intensity of the first crises was over I began to take Doran's positivity for granted.

On the third night I went to bed at midnight, I was anxious to be beside Lili when the hospital rattled into action. At six fifteen I went in to say 'good morning' to Doran for a moment first. His eyes were open.

'How is he?' I asked blithely. The nurse looked tired. 'There were some problems.'

'Problems?'

'He had a few little convulsions,' she said, 'and I'm concerned about his eyes.'

'His eyes?' 'He can't seem to shut them. I'm going to put patches over them. It must be very uncomfortable for him, as the light is so bright.' She was telling me that she thought Doran could see light, which was encouraging. At the same time his kidneys were not yet satisfactorily replaced by the machine; he was in trouble. The clock was coming round to six thirty. 'Is he all right for the moment?' I asked. 'He seems to be now. The registrar will be here in a moment.' I made a choice. 'I'm going over to my daughter. I'll be half an hour. Please call me if there's any problem.'

'Fine.'

Lili woke in my arms. 'How's Doran?' she asked.

'He's surviving, Lili,' I said, 'but now I need to go and give him a little push for both of us.'

When I came back, the room was full again. I walked round the group of medical staff and sat inconspicuously in a corner. They were trying out various alternatives to determine why Doran wasn't responding quickly enough. The registrar turned to me; I was getting used to being suddenly included in the conversation. 'We need to do a lumbar puncture,' he said. 'It's just a precaution to eliminate any danger of meningitis.' Meningitis was another of those familiar roads to brain injury that surrounded Doran.

'We can't use an anaesthetic and it may cause you some distress so perhaps you'd like to have some tea,' he went on.

'No, please,' I said, 'whatever happens to Doran happens to me.'

'Well, if you stay, it'll cause me some distress and I have to

48

do it,' said the Yorkshireman who was poised above Doran with his sleeves rolled up. I understood him; it was braver for me to go than to stay.

'For both of you,' I said. 'I'll do it'. I went out but it was impossible to do more than simply stand in the corridor, every part of me was directly attuned to the room. The nursing sister tried gentle persuasion to move me on, but seeing it was no good she used another tactic.

'You're an artist, aren't you? We need an artist up here to paint Cinderella's coach.' She pointed to some large sheets of white paper a little way from where the lumbar puncture was in progress.

The play leader arrived with some pots of paint and brushes and instructions; she stressed how difficult it had been to find someone to paint the coach. They were so kind and so charming I couldn't refuse. I took the brushes. The paint had charms; it was so long since I'd used any. I loved to discover images. Slowly I was drawn further and further into the painted story. While Doran was fighting his battles I was forgetting him. I was woken by the sound of screaming. It was the scream of someone very hurt and very angry – and by the intensity of it, it could only be Doran. I dropped the brush in horror but almost immediately the door of the room burst open and a nurse ran out.

'Oh,' she cried, 'I was coming to find you. Isn't it wonderful? It's normal!'

'Normal?' This seemed madness. 'Yes, it's a normal response at last.'

'Wasn't Doran normal before?' I asked. 'He didn't seem to be responding to pain,' she said. 'The doctor was very worried about him.'

'May I go in?'

'Not yet, but I felt I had to tell you.'

'Thank you,' I said. 'Thank you very much.'

She disappeared. I decided to go back to Lili who was about to have lunch. Lili was already much better; she was talking to the nurse. When she saw me she asked,'Is Doran having lunch?'

'He can't eat meals,' I said. 'He's sort of fed all the time through a tube in his head.'

'Why not his mouth?'

'Because he can't suck.'

'What are you having for lunch?'

The rattle of trolleys could be heard outside. The nurse said, 'It's macaroni, but we don't know if it's for pudding or main course.' The smell was curious. 'This is the best hospital in the world, but' – she went on confidently – 'I believe it came bottom in the Egon Ronay food guide.'

'Really?'

'Really, bottom,' she said.

I suggested Lili stick to the brussels sprouts. We were counting them out when we had another visitor, a tall, dark and handsome expatriot American I had known as my brother from my first months in London. I hadn't seen him for over two years, but news travels fast. Moe knew what I liked to eat and although he had never seen Lili he had guessed what might tempt her. He opened a large brown bag and produced bananas, grapes, Jewish bread and French cheese.

Lili opened her blue eyes wide and enchanted Moe. The feeling seemed so mutual I could leave them together. Moe undertook to come often and to shop for us; thus another material problem was solved.

Doran's condition stabilized during the day; he kept his main crises for the nights, which was very fair to Lili. In the hospital, night was not characterized by its darkness but by a change in its sounds. Now the voices of the children had gone; each new clatter had a startlingly clear geometric form and pitch.

I learned how to help the night nurse. I could hold Doran's arm out when he had his blood pressure taken. I could turn him and change the soft cotton wadding on which he lay. He didn't need a nappy, he had a catheter; the input and output of fluid had to be carefully measured. His incubator was also a weigh bed so that the slightest change in weight could be assessed. The balance of electrolytes was maintained by fine tubes entering through his navel. His internal temperature was registered constantly by wires entering his anus and externally fixed against his skin. Four electrodes on his chest monitored his heart beat. He had an intravenous drip to his head. Even his big toe had come in useful; it was wired up to register his pulse rate. Every twenty minutes the information had to be checked; Doran was also turned, comforted and washed. The nurse worked a ten hour shift; she was not allowed to leave Doran unattended. She didn't sit down. When I suggested it she laughed. 'If I did, I'd go to sleep.'

I liked learning what to do. At first we kept patches on Doran's eyes which still kept opening. One day she took the patches off and the eyes were closed.

'Today,' said the nurse, 'will be exciting. He goes for a kidney scan.'

I innocently expected the scanner to be on the same floor as the kidney unit, or perhaps at least in the same building. The fact was, that when our turn came, Doran was disengaged from what had seemed to be his life support system. Then, taking only his incubator, now on wheels, and the saline drip with him, we set off down the corridor. One nurse was supposed to achieve this perilous navigation alone and unassisted. Because I was there to open doors and steer round corners the drip did not actually get trapped or disconnected. Doran was still theoretically in considerable danger; every moment off the apparatus was a risk. At the bottom of Guy's tower we turned right and pressed on underground to the next building. I could tell the nurse was anxious by the humorous way she had of talking between her teeth. Rattled, banged and shaken about as he was, Doran remained sanguine throughout.

'He's great,' she said. 'Look at the way he keeps his nerve.'

We arrived victorious and intact at the scanning room to be told we were an hour early. There was some confusion. Doran's nurse was not prepared to wait. They rang for the registrar who appeared and disappeared very quickly. As a result it was indicated that Doran could be unloaded onto the scanner. For this he would have to come off the drip and out of the incubator.

The basement room was noticeably colder than the ward. His nurse insisted on waiting until the last possible moment before disconnecting him. She lay across Doran on the scanner to give him her own body heat and once the scan was taken she bundled him back into the incubator. We braced ourselves for the ascent to the Kidney Unit.

'How, when you take such good care of a patient, can you risk his life on expeditions like this?' I asked as the hundredth swing door snapped at our backs. 'It's insanity,' she said, 'but there's not enough money and we're understaffed.'

At last we were safely back and a small team was reuniting Doran to his framework of survival.

Guy's Hospital became a complete way of life. Everyone on the ward appeared courageous and perfectly unconscious of it. The only parts of me noticeably suffering were my hands. It was the rule that before one touched Doran one washed one's hands with incredibly strong disinfectant. Since Doran's blood pressure alone was taken every twenty minutes, I washed my hands rather often, and the skin was slowly disintegrating.

The Christmas decorations grew out into the ward. One afternoon I found a nurse fixing paperchains above Doran's incubator. The Yorkshire doctor and head registrar came in beaming.

They said, 'We've come about the milk, he can have it.'

'What milk?' asked the nurse.

'Mother's milk,' said the registrar.

'When, gentlemen?' I asked.

'Tomorrow, if you can fill a small bottleful. Oh, save my colleague some for his tea.'

For the next few days they kept changing their minds. I was perpetually producing small bottles which disappeared without reaching Doran. Christmas cards kept arriving. In one I found two tiny brown feathers attached to a twig giving the effect of a bird. We suspended it above Doran and it turned and twisted delicately in the warm air.

The number of crises by day or night had diminished. The problem now was less the immediate question of life, but the quality of life. Would his kidneys recover entirely? Was his brain any further hurt? I was also aware of being gently pushed to find some alternative accommodation for Lili and myself. It was explained that although Doran was probably out of immediate danger, what was needed was staying power and if I had friends then I should find someone prepared to look after me, at least at night. I felt God was making a perfectly good job of looking after me where I was. Then, the week before Christmas I found Bernard and Erica Kops planted in the corridor. They were holding a bottle of Veuve du Vernay and a bag of fresh dates.

'We've come to tell you you're spending Christmas with us. We're having the Christmas tree hung with stars of David.'

'You came from heaven?' I said.

'This must be hell,' said Bernard.

'No, it's more like purgatory, Bernard,' said Erica.

Bernard and his family had the knack of taking me in when I was most in need. 'Anyway,' I said, 'you were sent with divine purpose.' They thrust the bottle and the dates into my hands.

'From Paradise,' said Bernard. 'Come to Paradise on Christmas Day.' The arrangement was made.

There was enthusiasm about the state of Doran's kidneys. Although he couldn't blink, his eyes opened and shut and he was making sucking gestures. The nurse tried him with a dummy. He drew it in passionately as if it had been a part of his own body long mislaid. From the dummy he graduated to a little of my milk from the bottle. As he recovered I watched, half expecting him to leave behind the old stamp of his original brain injury. The hope was naïve, and I could see his medical team were worried.

'Do you find him changed in any way?' they pressed me. 'Is he the same baby you knew before?'

It would have been hard to describe the relationship I had had with Doran over the past months since it depended on so many invisible attunements. I remembered one thing he didn't like but tolerated out of some respect for the acknowledged

53

intimacy between mother and child. I picked his nose. Doran winced; if he had been granted more movement he would certainly have kicked me away. It was a familiar wince followed by an amiable resignation that indicated how clearly he recognized me.

'Doran is still very much himself,' I said. They looked a bit puzzled but relieved.

I packed my things and packed Lili's things. It was Christmas Eve. Lili had a large stocking ready to hang up.

When I went to find Doran, his room had mysteriously changed. He lay in a small bed wearing a very new blue polka dot suit. There was no drip and no life support system but the twig bird still spun to left and right above his head. At the foot of the bed was a stocking and several small coloured packages were stacked on his table. The nurse said, 'You can feed him today with the bottle and if he takes to it all right, tomorrow you can feed him yourself.'

I said, 'That's my Christmas present.'

I bent over to pick Doran up. Turning his head to me I saw its usual shape had gone; it seemed huge and lop-sided. I didn't know what to think. I hugged him to me while I wrestled with this new deformity.

The nurse passed me a bottle. I thought she seemed very cheerful considering my son had what appeared to be hydrocephalous. On the other hand it was part of life here to be cheerful regardless of adversity. I waited for an explanation but none came.

Doran somehow managed to nose the bottle into his mouth and began to feed. 'Look,' said the nurse, 'he's sucking well. He makes quite a noise.'

Doran was slurping loudly.

'Yes,' I said, 'but what about his head?'

'His head?' she said.

'His head,' I insisted. 'It's grown, hasn't it.'

The nurse studied me incredulously. Then she said, 'You mean where the drip came off? There's a little swelling.'

Relief flooded into me.

'I thought it rather terrific.'

'Yes,' she said soothingly. 'Perhaps a bit more than you'd expect but it will soon go down.'

I didn't realize fluid under the skin could be so hard. Doran rapturously finished his bottle and then another. By the end of the day he had a reputation for having an enormous appetite.

Christmas Day was amazing. It appeared that every patient who could possibly go, left the hospital at Christmas, and at the same time every charity that possibly could sent sacks of toys and men in Father Christmas suits to the hospital. It was Lili's third Christmas and she was left in no doubt of its meaning. From the moment she woke she was showered with presents. Father Christmases lay in waiting round every corner and as Lili advanced down the corridor she slowly disappeared behind a mountain of soft toys. Doran was granted total liberty to travel with us about the hospital. His nurse had dressed him in a stretch suit with a red waistcoat and red and yellow flowered sleeves. He looked abundantly festive and was very prepared to be carried around. I shared the bottle of Veuve du Vernay with the Yorkshire doctor and hoped Doran would take such a level of alcohol in his Christmas lunch. Whatever problems Doran might now face it appeared that his kidneys were generally the toast of the ward. Nobody had expected him to make such a recovery and they all felt free and safe enough to tell me so. The euphoria lasted until tea time when I was handing round cake. The registrar was on holiday and his replacement was a woman I hadn't met before. I handed her a slice without putting Doran down or disengaging him from his somewhat continuous meal.

'Why do you feed him all the time?' she asked.

'It's our Christmas present,' I said good-humouredly.

She looked at me curiously. I could see she wanted to say something and was trying to find a way of putting it. I didn't want her to put it any way, but she was determined to make her point.

'You do know he's unlikely to be normal,' she said. 'He's

had three really big assaults and any one of them could have harmed him pretty badly.'

'Three assaults?'

'Kernicterus, whooping cough and kidney failure,' she said quietly.

'Oh,' I said. 'Yes, I suppose he has.'

'Well, I think you ought to think about it,' she said.

'It's Christmas,' I said. 'Please, I'm not going to hear anything that's not positive about Doran. He's alive and I love him.'

'It may not be enough,' she said.

I moved on and handed out cake to someone else. Miraculously there were no patients with 'nil by mouth' hung over their beds. Lili appeared with a doll's pram. Behind her were the voices of carol singers and before long we were surrounded. They handed me a sheet of words and pressed us on to the next ward.

'It's so nice to have a baby with us,' they said. 'What's his name?'

Someone else said, 'It's snowing outside.'

Lili's legs grew tired so she climbed into the pram she was pushing and cuddled the doll. The conductor of the carol singers decided to take her over and, with Doran and I at her side, she lead the group, intent on Christmas joy, at full steam round the hospital.

I was wondering where we were when the paintings of Cinderella suddenly reappeared on the walls. We followed the story back to Doran's room. He was tired; it was an almost normal tiredness. He'd spent an entire day doing something for himself. His stomach was comfortably full and he accepted his bed and pillow. Leaving Doran behind was a curious experience.

I ordered a taxi to take us to where the Kops family lived. Bernard and the children were outside clearing the snow and throwing snowballs. He carried Lili in on his shoulders.

'Lili, you're a Billy but I love thee,' he chanted.

Lili said, 'Do you love Doran too?'

'Tonight,' he answered, 'is the night that I love every-one.'

By the morning the snow was still piling up and there was ice as well. The expedition back to Guy's was slow and difficult. It was obviously imperative that I didn't break a leg, but to keep both Lili and myself upright with any consistency was almost impossible. There was no let up in the weather. It snowed all afternoon. Getting home looked like an Arctic exploration. Lili and I were sitting on a pile of toys which some last desperate Father Christmases had left in the middle of the ward. Doran was sucking hard and feeling generously disposed towards the chaotic world in which his senses told him he lived, when Moe appeared.

Moe seemed totally at home with Doran. He handled him with firmness and enthusiasm; Doran loved it. It was a positive alternative to drinking. Watching him in Moe's arms I could learn a little more about how his senses worked. His eyes rolled about everywhere but when he was lifted up to the shiny balls which decorated kissing bushes, hung at intervals from the ceiling, he smiled; and when he was lowered away from them he complained.

I was now sure Doran could see. I didn't care what, or how much, I only cared that the visual pathways existed! It was there, I felt with certainty it could be stimulated.

'Look, Moe, he can see! Isn't it lovely he can see!'

Moe said, 'Of course he can see, Linda.'

I took Lili's hand and danced round Moe with wild enthusiasm.

'It's the best Christmas I've ever had,' I said.

Moe said, 'I believe you, Linda, I believe you.'

That day Doran was more enthusiastic about being up, and he was also considerably less enthusiastic about going back to bed. He had a taste for life, for adventure, whatever other perpetual problems he had; he knew where the bright lights and the action were. By half past six we had to set off for the Kops' home, if we were to arrive in some kind of relative safety. Moe came with us, carrying Lili over the snow. London was being restored to the ice age. The warm protection of the hospital faded behind a howling white storm.

Lili and I left for Guy's every morning, and every morning Moe met us at Bernard's door, his scarf up over his nose and ears, and well plastered with snow. With unbounded cheerfulness he helped us to the kidney unit, and every evening he was there to take us home.

Bernard had a huge box of satsumas in the hall, which we were instructed to eat constantly for moral support and vitamin 'c'. We fed them to each other on the underground and arrived with sticky fingers and pockets full of peel.

Doran had been moved to another room. I recognized it as the room I'd first been given at Guy's. He had become a hero to many of the other patients. He had returned from the gates of death, and that made him worth visiting; children began to ask after him and came in to shake his hands. The nurses tried to sit him in a straight backed plastic chair but it was impossible. Doran arched his back, slid to one side and screamed. From the moment we arrived in his room till the moment we left, Doran was in my arms. His favourite occupations were being held up to the Christmas decorations or gently boxed by one of the auxiliary staff. Since he couldn't open his hands, she decided his fists were boxing gloves and fought with him whenever she was passing. When we left he always protested, but the note was more of anger than of fear, and I trusted that he trusted us to come back. His nurse said she had never encountered a baby who drank so much, or, so noisily. They said the sound of his drinking could be heard two wards away. He was well, or well enough to go home.

I had mixed feelings about home when I thought of the cold, and the lack of money and the separation from my friends. But then I remembered the smell of the country and thought how beautiful the fields must look under the snow. I thought of the forest as a kind of guardian for us. I thought of the coloured walls of my cottage and the paintings hanging there, and the big double bed we could all three fall into, and then I wanted very much to be home. It was January, the Christmas decorations were coming down and I said goodbye to Doran's consultant. He said, 'You know your son is quite remarkable; there is no way he could have been expected to be leaving so soon.'

'He has lived through so much already,' I said. 'I can't believe that he's not going to do something extraordinary with his life.'

The consultant was young, he had blue eyes and fair hair, it was probably against his scientific training to agree with me, but he said, 'Nor can I.'

5

THE TAXI ARRIVED, its lateness had been predictable; London was enduring the worse weather conditions for fifteen years. We were warmly dressed to the point of discomfort, and Moe was coming home with us which delighted Lili. We settled into the back seat and set off towards Croydon and on along the A23, the snow driving into the windscreen wipers and Radio 1 optimistically playing full blast.

Doran was eager to try out as many positions as possible. The only sort of movement he could actually make himself was to arch his back and wriggle just enough to slide. He slid across my shoulders, over Lili's chest and down into Moe's lap. He had a superabundance of energy, explosively confined by his restricted movement; there was no chance of rocking him to sleep.

Our interest unexpectedly switched when the car slithered round a steep bend. The engine cut out and we came to a halt on the edge of a snowdrift. We were miles from home. The only sign of hope was what looked like a small farm perched on a snowy hillside about a quarter of a mile down the road. I pointed out this refuge and with some relief suggested that our driver could phone another taxi to pick us up; preferably the nearest taxi foolhardy enough to be on the road. It was still snowing lightly. The picture of us all, or at least Doran, dying of hypothermia appeared to me as a plausible finale, but the driver was a proud man who refused to admit defeat. He insisted that his taxi had some small familiar fault which could be corrected very simply. Bidding us be of good cheer, he climbed out. Since he evidently found it reasonable to stand with his head under the bonnet in the freezing snow, I could only conclude he must be fairly confident. Time went by; after about ten minutes he tried the engine again. It repeated a lonely choking sound three times and then died away. I tentatively suggested recourse to the telephone. The driver insisted that it would take at least an hour to find another taxi and that another five minutes would yield results.

'It's amazing that he knows what to do,' I said, 'and he's out there doing it.'

Moe felt pretty helpless about cars. He reached into his rather old and battered black hold-all and produced a bag of small chewy rings of Jewish bread called bagels, and a large slice of interesting red cheese.

Lili said, 'I'm hungry', and her hands were filled with food. Doran was bored now that the motion of the car had stopped. It was getting noticeably colder, the five minutes became twenty minutes. The man outside refused all offers of refreshment and advice. He returned twice to the driving seat only to elicit the same melancholy sound from the car engine.

I could see evening drawing on, the snow building up and the road being cut off. Then Lili said she wanted to pee. This meant a marathon effort of unzipping and unwrapping layers of clothing before the plea was too late. Moe opened the car door and lowered her over the snow which blew mischievously round her bottom and in across the seat and floor. I assumed our driver must have stoically frozen to death by now. When, quite suddenly he climbed in and said, 'It won't start. I think our best bet is to go and ring for another cab. Do you have any money?'

'But you've been paid to take us home.'

'I've no cash for alternative transport I'm afraid.'

Moe said, 'I've got money, Linda.' This was sufficient incentive. The driver disappeared towards the small farm which by now had lighted windows.

There was no passing traffic. An hour went by. The A23 seemed more like the road to Petrograd in a particularly foul and sinister Russian winter. I began to hear wolves and feel frostbite, when the sound of a fully functioning car engine became increasingly louder and more real. Eventually it stopped beside us. Both taximen appeared, our man had wisely decided to be picked up at the farm. I had no idea of what he intended to do; we left him standing by the inert mass of his machine.

Doran was briefly exposed to the snow. A flake or two touched his nose and cheek. The sensation was unfamiliar and out of his control. He threw back his head and roared angrily at the sky. The new driver brought us to our door without complaint but as he left he nodded towards the hill, 'You won't get a car up there again by morning if it freezes.'

'I think it is freezing,' I said. I was clutching the garden gate to stand upright. 'Thank you, and a happy New Year.'

'A happy New Year to you too, lady,' he said, and reversed away up the road with the minimum of wheel spin.

I opened the door. The cottage had no porch and you stepped straight into the living room. Inevitably the prevailing weather conditions stepped in after you.

We shut the weather out and heaved a triumphant sigh.

The interior was almost exactly as I'd left it. The best way to celebrate our safe return was by washing and cleaning everything. Lili wanted to go to sleep on the sofa with a patchwork rug and her favourite teddy bear; Doran wanted entertainment. I turned on every available source of heat including the oven, and lit a fire. For the next two hours I simply cleaned and threw away. It was luxury to be able to move freely about in my own house, and have Doran follow me from the independent heights of Moe's arms. Finally I found a tin of milk powder and made some tea. Lili woke, and we sat together round the fire drinking tea and eating the last of the bagels. The last of the bagels was in fact the last of the food. I had intended to stop at the general store where I had an account, and could buy groceries but I had forgotten. It seemed impossible to forget something so fundamental, but I had. Before hunger of any kind could replace the delicious sense of warmth which was now radiating from all sides, the front door banged open. A blizzard arrived on the hearth.

The door shut with equal ferocity and the blizzard melted. Judy and Peter, whom I had telephoned from Guy's, were standing before the fire with a large comforting-looking box.

'We walked across the fields,' said Peter. 'You can't get the car down the lane.'

'But that won't bother you,' said Judy, 'because *you* aren't going anywhere. You are going to stay home and be a mother.'

'You mean we stay home and starve to death. What a glorious blow to strike for maternity.'

'Peter and I are going to do your shopping for you. If you go out you'll freeze to death.'

Peter said, 'This weather's set in for the winter. It'll snow for the next three months.'

Judy began to produce packets of groceries from the bag. At the bottom was a mysterious oven-proof dish which she handed to Peter to take to the kitchen.

'We've been surviving on bagels,' I said.

'Bagels,' Judy almost screamed. 'Do you have bagels?'

'Sure,' said Moe, 'there's two more left in the bag.' Judy flung herself on the bag, between mouthfuls she said, 'You're American?' And so it was that the two expatriates and Peter began to discuss our immediate future as if it was their life's work.

Before supper was finished, they had established that they really were going to keep us indoors until the spring. Moe could come down every weekend; Judy and Peter would walk over the fields and bring supplies.

'Now that you've stopped your gallivanting all over the place,' said Judy, 'you can put a little time into your health. You and Lili are still coughing.'

Peter was right about the weather. The house became our world, and there I tried to find another world, one which would cure Doran.

I rose early, mainly because Doran was awake and bored. The two of us tried to make the fire before Lili woke. Doran's responsibilities were not to knock my teeth out with his head and not to scream.

When Lili appeared and we'd had breakfast, we bathed and changed Doran. This took up a considerable amount of time. The oval plastic bath stood on a towel in front of the fire. Doran had the privilege of being undressed by Lili. The press studs of his stretch suit were burst open one by one. She wrestled to squeeze his vest over his head and untie the piece of plastic which knotted over his nappy. Then we played a game called 'who can make Doran laugh most'. This involved kissing, tickling, and patting him. Lili usually won.

The bath was rather more extravagant. It was difficult to support Doran in the water with one hand, so we agreed that I would do the holding while Lili did the bathing. Unfortunately since both my hands were occupied, I had very little control as to what went on between Lili, Doran and the bathwater. Lili's only criterion was that Doran enjoyed it. She thought the more company Doran had in his bath, the better. When she asked if she could put all her ducks in the water, I said, 'Of course, darling.'

So she put all the ducks in the bath, including the pink knitted ones. These turned out to be only theoretical swimmers. They could however be rubbed with soap and squeezed over Doran's head. Lili made a lather that created a city of foam castles across the carpet. She brought her plastic tea service in and gave a tea party with Doran as King Neptune having cups of brine thrown at him in all directions. Her games were endlessly inventive and enduringly wet; anything left unbaptized was taken care of when lifting Doran out.

At that time my cottage had four rooms and a bathroom. If we kept the fire up and took the fan heater with us for extra warmth, we could stage different entertainments in each room. Both children liked a sense of arrival and departure, of pressing forward round the world. We never felt cooped up; there was always the possibility of moving on.

Doran had a small cot downstairs and a new altruistic ability to yawn and close his eyes just before Lili's bedtime.

Whether I took a longer or shorter time settling her, he would sleep serenely until I attempted to have a late and private tea. For some reason my son thought it was underhand of me to eat alone. When Judy and Peter arrived they invariably found us in front of the fire, Doran glued to my breast and me with a plate of bread, peanut butter and lettuce.

Judy decided I was starving myself. I said, 'I like it, it's nutritious, and besides that I only get £27 on social security.'

'You could earn more.'

'Judy, I am destined to a life of poverty and motherhood.'

She pursed her lips. 'You could manage with a little less of the poverty; so could we.'

Peter said, 'We found a chap who wants a wardrobe painted.'

'A wardrobe? Where would we put a wardrobe?'

The wardrobe fitted in the centre of the living room floor. The edifice was plain wood but looked more like a pagoda than a wardrobe. It belonged to an antique dealer who wanted it transformed into a piece of elegant eighteenth-century red lacquer work. I happened to be good at Chinese brushwork and knew how to age a painting in keeping with its imagined history. By divulging some secrets to Judy and Peter, we were able to undertake the transformation at night.

While Lili slept Doran was carried round the wardrobe. I cleaned my sable brushes and began to draft out a few birds and willow trees.

When the red and gold paint had been varnished it made a glittering centrepiece. Long after everyone had gone home Doran retained the idea that the wardrobe was still for his entertainment. While I was moving him around it he would lie with his head across my shoulder until I was sure he must have fallen asleep. But as I drew him gently towards the cot his eyes opened wide, the pupils rolled about, and warning noises sounded from his throat. One evening he did sleep even when I laid him down.

I decided that since we had a deadline to complete the commission, I might as well begin antiquing the roof. It was lovely to be working with such unexpected space and freedom.

I climbed the ladder; I could see Doran way below, although his face was partly hidden behind a thin red blanket. I began to reach further across, pushing my pots of varnish and paint in front of me. The varnish I used for antiquing was very strong stuff. I had a sudden sense of foreboding, at the same moment my elbow capsized the bottle. It fell directly on to Doran's blanket, inevitably it must have fallen into his eyes.

He didn't move, the sleep seemed exceptionally deep. I scrambled down the ladder and bent over him. The only solvents I could think of were as bad as the varnish. His eyes were now in danger of being physically damaged, and I was totally responsible. I pulled back the blanket. The thick liquid had sunk through it on to his cheek. A normal baby, sleeping with its head comfortably back on the pillows, would have had red varnish seeping into both its eyes. But Doran couldn't lie normally. His head was so far turned that only the side of his cheek and the rim of his ear were caught. Doran had a charmed life. It was terrifying; it was also magic.

We spent three months inside the house. The red pagoda wardrobe was completed and we were paid. Judy improved our diet. Peter brought us extra fuel. Nevertheless, I knew our electricity consumption far exceeded my ability to pay the bill. I hoped to find some loophole in the small print of the social security handbook. It was illogical that the state should spend so much public money to keep Doran alive in hospital, and then send him home to die of the cold. Logic was no help. The Department of Social Security was emphatically not the Salvation Army. We were caught in an intricate poverty trap from which there was no middle way of escape. A low paid part time job simply resulted in a cut in supplementary benefit. Doran's problem could not be officially recognized until he was two years old, when he would be entitled to an attendance allowance.

It began to be clear that since no one had ever seen a brain injured child recover, any work done with one was considered largely a waste of time, and could therefore be put off as long as possible.

Spring came abruptly. Sun and wind cleared the land of

snow. Just standing outside with sun on my cheeks was beautiful. Peter dug out my car and started it. The winter had been long and dark but we had not been alone. Life now stretched on ahead but its quality depended upon what we did with Doran, and whether it was successful.

My son was happier; he communicated that he would have had a great deal of interest in the world, if only he could get at it. He became interested in alternatives to breast milk, and I cooked him the most nutritious meals I could invent.

Doran took food very seriously. When he knew I was preparing it, he was calm. If the final result was not to his taste he protested until I returned it to the stove. Once it became acceptable it disappeared desperately fast.

'Doran,' I cried, 'against all my principles I am slaving over a hot stove for the whims of a male child.'

Lili said, 'Do you slave for my whims, mummy?'

'You don't have whims, Lili.'

'Why does Doran?'

'He has problems with communication,' I said, 'but we're going to resolve it.'

The next few weeks were uncomfortable. The better weather brought my health visitor, in whose eyes Doran was evidently doomed. I made a ritual visit to my doctor who said he wasn't putting Doran on the scrap heap but I ought to start looking after myself. I replied that by looking after Doran, I was looking after myself. Furthermore if I wasn't to look after Doran, who else was? Nobody apparently! I could see that Doran wasn't growing, that he had no control over his head, that his hands were still fists, and that there were no messages to link the different parts of his body except the sudden reflex in his back. Neurologically Doran was a mess, and psychologically he was beginning to realize it.

On the first day it was fine enough to put a rug out in the garden, Doran lay on it and howled. I have never heard him cry like that before or since. It was a cry from the heart. Perhaps he had had some hope that things would change more quickly. He arched his back and pushed his face into the

67

ground. Lili was playing in the flower bed with several pots and a bucket of water. I had to do something else for Doran, something to change his life and to make each day worth the experience. My eye went from Lili to Doran and back to Lili. I remembered the endless baths before the open fire, the favourite pastime of all children; the one they had in common was water. I would take them swimming! My instinct was to leave at once for the nearest swimming pool. The only one that I could think of was thirteen miles away in Crawley. There would be the cost of the petrol and the cost of the entrance fee, but I didn't consider them.

'Lili,' I said, 'would you like to go swimming?'

'Now?'

'Almost now, I'm going to find some costumes.'

Before Doran could descend to any further depths of tragedy, I dragged him upstairs to look for some reasonable clothing for the expedition. I found an old costume for myself, armbands and a pair of towelling pants for Lili, and nothing for Doran. I saw no reason why he shouldn't swim in nothing.

Lili was jubilant. It was early afternoon and we had plenty of time.

It had been two years since I had been to the swimming baths; I had forgotten the humidity, the smell of chlorine, the noise, the small cubicles and the wet floors onto which dry clothes inevitably slithered. I tried to smuggle Doran in as a babe in arms, but a swimmer needed a ticket and Doran was a swimmer. I heard other mothers shouting at their children. 'Don't go without me.' 'Don't run, the floor's slippery.' 'Don't drop the towel in the water.'

I began to see it wasn't all wine and roses. Doran was prepared to be accommodating, unless he was put down and I couldn't continue to hold him if we were ever going to get our clothes off. The only safe place was a playpen in the middle of the floor. I lowered him stoically into it and waited for the characteristic explosion of wrath. Doran didn't murmur. He evidently approved of the noise, the smell, and the temperature. Lili was eventually ready with her armbands blown up.

We moved with caution across the slithery floor, through the showers and foot baths and out into the great noisy hall where the floor ended and a large pool of water began. With Doran under one arm, and Lili's hand firmly grasped in mine, we edged round the side and towards the area allocated to beginners. At this time of day it was very quiet.

The children's pool had a barrier around it. Swimmers climbed a ladder over the side of the barrier and dropped into the water. I realized by the even way the water reached the waists of the three other wading mothers, that the pool had a constant depth. It was a depth likely to reach over Lili's nose, she had to keep her armbands on, or sink. I could see she was intrigued by the way they blew up, and was very likely to let them down. I did not want to improve Doran by drowning Lili, so we sat on the side and talked.

'Lili, this is the first time Doran has ever been to the swimming pool, so we must stay beside him all the time. And remember that your armbands are magic, so don't touch them and don't take them off.'

'Why doesn't Doran have armbands?'

'Doran's too small. He has us to keep him up.'

Lili suddenly jumped and moved off as naturally as if she had done so every day of her life. I slid down slowly, feeling the tepid water as it climbed up my bathing costume. I hesitated for a moment holding Doran just above the surface. He looked concerned. I ducked him and brought him up, he yelled with delight. I did it again and again.

'Lili!' I called. 'Doran likes it!'

The more we went swimming the more relaxed my son became. Extravagantly I bought season tickets with the money I had saved for the electricity bill; now I couldn't pay any of it but I didn't care.

The Crawley Leisure Centre includes a multitude of different sports facilities, a refreshment room, and right next door to the changing room, a crèche and play school. Lili looked in; she was transfixed by the sight of children and an indoor slide. So we spent whole days in Crawley; Doran went swimming twice, but Lili played in the crèche in the mornings, and the pool in the afternoons.

I saw that the water would make it easier for Doran to move his limbs and would stimulate his skin, increasing sensation all over his body. The result would be like returning to the amniotic fluid in the womb and would perhaps produce the rebirth of another part of his brain. Hydrotherapy seemed ideal for spastic children but no one had offered it or recommended it to me, and I had never heard of it being attempted with the degree of intensity which I was proposing. There was a chance it would have an effect.

Our days were now centred upon getting to the baths. We took a picnic lunch, and after the first swim we sat upstairs in the refreshment room, and ate it looking down on the table tennis and badminton from the balcony. I felt sure Doran was watching but what he was seeing remained a mystery. The preferred position of his pupils appeared to be two half moons on either side of the bridge of his nose.

I presumed his hearing must be equally strange but since he couldn't control either his eyes or his head, it was hard for him to locate sounds or connect them to any particular event. I began to realize how many connections are necessary to perform even the smallest physical task.

Meanwhile Doran was gaining in prestige at the pool. Because of his immobility he was taken for a much younger baby. The clue to his abnormality, was his vision. People found their own solution to the problem. 'What a beautiful baby. It's a pity, about his eyes, but you can have an operation to correct them.' There was great faith in the efficacy of this operation. I knew that no surgery to his eye muscles could reach the source of the trouble. Nevertheless I was strangely pleased to have Doran mistaken for a relatively normal baby of two months old, instead of a severely brain injured one of seven months.

The confusion increased; it was hard to intervene. 'What a long baby!' mothers exclaimed as they passed him in the playpen. Doran saw no confusion; he was admired.

'Are you trying to turn him into an Olympic swimmer?' 'He doesn't mind the water, does he?' 'Watch out for the baby!'

We spent about an hour in the pool each session, and a great deal more time getting in and out. Doran liked to be pulled along with his chin on the surface, he liked to be ducked, to glide on his back, to be splashed. He loved it when the schools came out and the baths were crowded with exuberant boys. The louder, rougher and tougher they were, the more he laughed. The schoolboys began to respect him.

'It's that baby again. He's tough isn't he? Are you his mother?'

'No, she's his coach.'

'When's the channel swim?'

Whatever he heard, Doran knew it was praise. If we were jostled as we passed a group having a fight, Doran jumped to my defence; he arched his back and splashed furiously with his fists. Lili took an equally serious interest in the boys. She let her blonde curls bob on the suface, then she would dip her head down, take a mouthful and blow a waterspout. The effect was utterly disarming. Young admirers began running up to the car to ask when she'd be coming again.

We were caught up in our own routine when the electricity bill arrived. Since I had no savings, I put my case before the DHSS.

They were disinterested in the amount it would cost to keep a child in care.

A mother working with a brain injured child was untrained, and therefore unsalaried and unrecognized. I realized they would rather see a child go into care than assess the contribution of the child's family. I appealed for a petrol allowance. Without a car, I would have to push a pram with two children up a steep winding country lane one and a half miles to a bus stop, and a further five miles to the nearest town. They suggested I sell the cottage.

Selling a cottage is a protracted affair. What should I do in the meantime? My mortgage was very low and if I chose any accommodation on the main road, the cost would be more than double. Since the DHSS would have been obliged to pay, the fact that I owned such a small cottage was to their advantage. The contradictions were endless. I stopped fighting for myself and resumed fighting injustice everywhere.

'In such cases,' I said, 'you leave no alternatives but death or prison. There is no legal way I can save my family.' They said it was unfortunate, but they were only doing their job.

Mavis, my social worker, had been a regular visitor during our long winter sojourn in the house and had grown attached to us. She wrote away to various charities on our behalf. They repeated that no one could help until Doran was two years old and in receipt of an Attendance Allowance.

'Is Doran supposed to lie in a cot until he's two years old?' I asked. 'Look at the effect of the swimming.'

The swimming had changed Doran. He was communicating with people. He smiled more than he cried. He ceased to cry the moment his request was granted. I didn't think he made unreasonable requests; they were the same ones I would have made in his position.

Mavis phoned one morning full of excitement. 'I tried a rather long shot,' she said, 'but I think it will work. The charity is the Artists General Benevolent Fund.'

I was dumbfounded. 'You mean there's a Benevolent Fund for artists?'

'Yes, I do, and you are an artist. You've had exhibitions, you've taught in art colleges, you paint pictures and furniture, and you're on hard times. You qualify.'

'I thought all artists were on hard times,' I said.

But I did qualify.

They wanted to pay off my electricity in one lump but the social security did not find it acceptable. The maximum allowance for a week was £64, anything over that would simply be deducted from my supplementary benefit. I would be no better off. After some negotiations they allowed the Electricity Board to take a weekly percentage from the benefit before I received it. This would both go towards paying off my present bill, and cover any future ones. The Benevolent Fund continued to press to help me more substantially. We were in the position of having a fairy godmother with her wand hand tied.

Then miraculously someone read the small print again, and found that a charity was entitled to give me a travel allowance, and to back date it. The Artists Benevolent Fund jubilantly agreed and the dispute had a happy ending.

Not long afterwards we went to renew our monthly season ticket at the baths. The cashier smiled down upon us and asked the usual question.

'Are you training him to swim the channel?'

This time, because I was so positive about Doran's swimming, because the sun was shining, and I liked her face, I told her the story.

She said, 'Then you shouldn't be paying.' And she went to see the manager.

The manager said it was the town's policy to admit handicapped children and their teachers free, and in his eyes I was Doran's teacher. When we left the baths that day a line of army cadets was trooping through the turnstile. I expected them to ignore a baby. Instead they stopped us. 'Has he been swimming? Take a look at that baby.' One by one they saluted Doran as I carried him out.

At the end of such a good week I had an appointment with the consultant who had originally made the diagnosis and given a prognosis on Doran's future. The change in his patient seemed so evident, I felt sure that he would be persuaded to modify the verdict to one of hope.

Doran was weighed, this time he was allowed to keep his clothes on; he maintained a good humour. I felt very cheerful, Doran was pronounced 'helpful', and Lili played on the swivel chair. I was waiting for the optimistic response. Although I knew that brain-injured children were not expected to recover I said, 'He's much better.'

'He seems much happier,' said the consultant calmly.

'He's that too.'

'You look fitter.'

'Only because Doran's better.'

73

He paused and then said, 'It's really about time he had some physiotherapy. I'll put you in touch with the doctor at the cerebral palsy hospital.'

The cerebral palsy hospital was a large hospital school for spastics and children with allied complaints.

'Is that really necessary?' I said. 'After all, I'm taking him swimming.'

I was still afraid. I wondered what I might see at the cerebral palsy hospital, and if it might in some way cling to Doran.

'They have a pool there. I'm sure they'd let you use it. I'll get in touch with their consultant for you.'

'I'm prepared to go there if I can take him swimming. I think the swimming is vital.'

When I left I realized that he hadn't really told me anything about Doran at all. He had been very considerate and I had been too polite to ask any questions. Now I could only wait for the report he would send to my doctor. I was a little unhappy about this but the feeling faded. The report would take about a week to arrive, in the meantime I was well occupied.

Doran found that in addition to the baths, he liked the showers. I stood holding him up to the warm water gently pressing his hands open and shut, so that the palms received stimulation. It occurred to me that no one had actually told me why Doran was stiff. They told me he had become stiff because his brain was injured. And they confirmed the fact that he was stiff, except of course in his neck, which wasn't stiff enough even to support his head. But why? What was happening? Nobody appeared to know; what was worse was that nobody seemed curious. Once a child was brain injured his symptoms were documented to establish the degree of injury. The documentation could go on endlessly: but that was all. I couldn't see that the doctors knew any more than parents.

One morning we were later leaving the pool. A school had come in and the children were passing through the changing rooms. At first I thought they were blind. Many of them seemed to be groping rather than walking; their mouths were

74

open, their faces, whether grinning or frowning, communicated nothing. They moved as if they lived in a precarious, insubstantial, threatening world, through which they were being unwillingly dragged by their teachers. They were the brain injured children of today, or rather a sample of the lucky ones who could walk. They had arrived to remind me of something. As I dried Doran I studied the children. Fear of them slowly left me. I wanted to understand. Looking at them, it seemed impossible that these were Doran's brothers. But it was true. Whatever I did for Doran, I would, and could do for them.

The idea made me wildly happy and then remorseful. I packed up the things knowing that whatever I did in future they would be left behind. I was walking out on them.

On the way home it was time to call at my doctor's and discuss the results of the consultant's report. We were five minutes late which gave us a black mark. My doctor said he'd heard we were going swimming but wasn't twice a day a little excessive?

I said, 'I think brain injury is a little excessive.'

We got down to the report. Slowly, I began to realize that the consultant I'd talked to so blithely had a very different picture of Doran from the one I'd anticipated. Every symptom pointed to a severe and hopeless condition, which a doctor could not easily confront.

We began to come to the point.

'Doran has the beginning of Athetoid movement.'

'Athetoid, what's Athetoid?' I asked.

'It means if he wanted to reach out for something his hand wouldn't be able to move straight towards it.'

'What would it do?'

The doctor made a curiously ugly gesture bending his wrist and elbow back, 'Something like that,' he said.

'Why?'

'Because of the injury to the motor part of his brain.'

'But why that gesture and not another?'

'That's the way it affects the muscles.'

'I see,' I said, although I didn't. I supposed I couldn't ask the right questions because I could never get suitable answers.

'But why can't Doran get better?'

He looked at me with a mixture of pity and apprehension.

'Once the cells are dead they can't regenerate.'

'So they keep telling me but what about the other cells?'

He didn't know about the other cells. I wished he could tell me who did.

We went home and I organized supper. I knew I should be doing something more, but what, and how, and in what order. I kept thinking about it while I poached the eggs. Doran liked poached egg with wheatgerm. We had just sat down when the phone rang. Doran and I left our plates on the table, but Lili carried hers with her. We made a family group round the telephone receiver.

The caller said, 'Hello, it's Judith.'

'Judy?' I said, confused because of the American accent.

'Judith.'

'Oh, *Judith*, are you in New York?'

'No, I'm back. We're here in East Grinstead.'

When Peter was alive we had both met Judith through a mutual interest in natural childbirth. I had Lili; Judith suffered a series of miscarriages. After Peter's death it had seemed natural that Judith and Michael should become Lili's godparents. They also became Doran's godparents although they had never met him. They had accepted the responsibility for an unborn child before they left for America. At first it was possible to write a little of the events surrounding Doran's birth, but as his life grew increasingly problematic I had given up.

'What's happening to you?' she asked.

'I go swimming, twice a day.'

'Swimming?'

'I don't exactly go swimming. To be truthful, Doran and Lili go swimming, I simply walk around in the water.'

'Did you say "on" or "in" the water?'

'I walk around in the water holding Doran.'

She paused, and then said, 'Can we come round and talk about it?'

'I think you'd better.'

Lili picked up her plate and we went back to the table. We had moved to the fire when Judith and Michael arrived.

It was hard to explain how serious Doran's condition looked, how hopeless everyone thought it was, and how I persisted in a perverse and total optimism. Judith put her finger in Doran's fist. He clenched it and clung on.

'He's got a good grip,' she said.

'It's not so much that he's got a good grip, as that he can't let go.'

'He holds on because he wants to make it,' she said. 'You're going to make it, Doran.'

We were united in this aim.

Judith and Michael lived half way between the swimming pool and my home. We met nearly every day. She cooked for us and encouraged us, and, while Michael and Lili played the piano, we talked about Doran. We had fallen into noticing the minutest changes. If anything kept us from despair it was Doran himself. He demanded to be everybody's equal. He was also showing great interest in Judith's cooking.

My appointment to take Doran to the cerebral palsy hospital finally came. We reached Judith's late. It was an afternoon in early June. She was in the garden weeding the roses and she ran down the path to meet us.

'I've news,' she said. 'And it's just what you want.'

I smiled, 'I can only think of news I don't want.'

'That's because the only stuff you want is help for Doran.'

'I suppose so.'

'Well, this is it.'

'What? How? When? Where?'

'That's better. Be quiet then and I'll tell you. There's a place in America where brain injured children of two and three years old are learning to read and do maths.'

'What?'

'They teach the parents how to develop the uninjured part

77

of the brain to take over . . . And the children learn to run and swing from ladders.'

'How, Judith, how?'

'I don't know. You're going there to find out.'

'I certainly am,' I said laughing. 'But how did you find out?'

'My friend Dianna Phillips – who's an incredible person, you'd love her – just wrote to her mother-in-law, who's my friend Nita, about it. I was there when Nita opened the letter.'

'Why did she write about it?'

'She's an artist and a teacher and, like you, she thinks children are underestimated, so now she works there.'

'Does she know about Doran?'

'Not yet, but she's going to.'

'What's this place called?'

'It's got an impressive name; it's called the "Institutes for the Achievement of Human Potential".'

'That's a lovely name,' I said, 'but I need more information.'

Judith rang Dianna that night and the following morning she rang me. The first thing I had to do was to get hold of a book called *What To Do About Your Brain Injured Child*. It was written by a man called Glenn Doman, who was the director of the Institutes. The next thing to do was write to him and ask for an appointment.

'Wait a minute,' I said, 'I'm living on social security. How do I fly to America?'

'Are you really worried about how to find the money?'

'No,' I said. 'I'll find the money; it's my destiny to find it.'

The book was published in England. At each post I waited like a cat by a mouse hole until it arrived through my letter box. The next problem was how to read it. Doran was still no sleeper.

I took the book to bed with me hoping to make some sense of the first chapter before I was disturbed. Doran seemed very happy; he settled in to have a drink, and closed his eyes. I read the first sentence.

'On one Monday in this coming month, as on one Monday of every month, ninety-nine people will arrive in the Institutes for the Achievement of Human Potential Philadelphia . . .'

And I didn't stop until I had reached the end.

For the first time in his entire life Doran had slept all night. This was surprising because every five minutes I found myself flinging the book in the air and crying, 'It's true, it's true.' Here was someone who had asked the right questions. They were simple, beautiful, elegant. They were brilliant. And yet they echoed the same simple-minded words that parents of brain injured children half formulate, but dare not ask before the faces of their children's physicians.

I had a phone by my bed and I used it to call Judith. Judith didn't have a phone by her bed. She sounded as if she had just fallen down the stairs.

'Judith!' I began. 'It's outrageously early.'

'Yes.'

'But you got up?'

'I knew it was you. Who else would phone so early?'

'Judith, I've read the book. I read it all night. It's absolute champagne. I'm drunk, I've been drunk all night. This man asked all the right questions.'

'And what about the answers?' she said.

'That's the bonus, Judith. He found them, and I know he's right. He's wonderfully, unbearably, right.' I paused for breath. 'Are you sure you're all right Judith? You sound as if you just fell down the stairs.'

Judith said, 'It is outrageously early. I told you I knew it was you and that's why I *have* just fallen down the stairs.'

6

---*---

THE PLACE where children learned to crawl was under my feet.

What one did for one's brain injured child was to reorganize the healthy part of the brain to take over the functions of the part lost through injury. How one did it was to pattern the brain with all the right information that a normal well child would collect in its development. The key was the frequency, intensity and duration of the stimulus.

The first vital patternings were those that would induce Doran to crawl. Until he could crawl and for some time afterwards, his entire life would be spent on the floor.

My son was not altogether enthusiastic about being liberated in this new athletic field. He complained with all the frequency, intensity and duration he could summon.

Lili and I were usually on the floor, shoulder to shoulder in front of him; all he was required to do was to lift his head up. This was difficult, but not impossible. The book also suggested flashing lights intermittently into his eyes to stimulate the visual pathways; from time to time he and I disappeared into the broom cupboard with a torch.

Judith spent hours on the phone to Dianna who was coming to England the following month. I postponed writing to the Institutes until we met.

We went on visiting the baths. Doran now believed that he was intended to grow up as some kind of fish.

The swimming had a beneficial effect upon another of his problems; it helped to stimulate his bowel movements. The sounds of his going into this labour invariably began on the way home. They were a signal for me to stop the car, remove his nappy, and perform an act of midwifery with all the necessary zeal I remembered from my natural childbirth classes.

'Come on now, Doran, pant: one, two, three – now push, push hard. You're doing fine.'

I arrived home with curious looking paper parcels which were consigned to the bin without being unwrapped.

By the time of our appointment at the hospital arrived, I felt confident. Doran had finally graduated to a car seat. Lili sat up beside him reciting dozens of nursery rhymes while I followed the map which brought us to the doors of the physiotherapy unit.

We were on time. The room was large with big windows. Lili saw the toys, I saw the calipers standing in brightly lit corners. A child of about ten years old, with both her legs well armoured, walked slowly back and forth between a pair of hand rails.

We introduced ourselves. I had Doran tucked under my arm in the crawling posture. It suggested an active form of transportation and was as far away from an image of pathos as I could imagine.

We were assigned a physiotherapist called Carol. She was still occupied with a little girl. I took Doran across to them and put him down on the floor on his stomach. Lili climbed into the toy box.

The little girl was being instructed to sit up. Her spine curved, and her head hung down over her chest. Her hands were repeatedly put out, one at each side to steady her, then the physiotherapist gently let go of her shoulders and she fell forwards on to her face.

Carol's nature was warm and friendly. Her patient remained obstinately uncooperative.

The little girl's mother turned to me, 'She's very good. They just don't seem to know what's the matter with her.'

Carol smiled, 'That'll be all for now.' The woman picked up the little girl and left the building.

'Surely,' I said, 'that child was brain injured?'

'That's a bit general.'

'How old was she? Three?'

'Five.'

'Five? She's so small.'

'She isn't very big, is she?'

'Why?'

'Some children grow more than others.'

'Would you expect Doran to grow?'

'I think you ought to ask the doctor.'

'Why were you getting her to sit up?'

'Mothers prefer to see their children sitting so that they can use their hands.'

'It seemed a little premature.'

Carol smiled, 'The doctor will be here in a moment; you can discuss it with her. She's very good; we're very privileged to have her.'

The doctor arrived. Behind her staggered a small dark haired woman carrying the body of a very long, very stiff child whose weight was not decreased by a scaffolding of leg irons. The child's eyes turned up, its tongue lolled out, its arms looked unusually jointed. The load was altogether difficult.

Our doctor tucked her notes under her arm and smiled cheerfully at the departing team.

'Goodbye, Mrs Smith. I'm glad to see Mary's coming along well.'

Now if there was one thing Mary didn't look like it was a person 'coming along well'.

'Has she been coming here long?' I asked.

'Oh, Mary's been with us for years,' said Carol in the same cheerful tones.

The doctor came over to us. We shook hands. After a few questions she said, 'Let's see what he can do.'

'Not much at present, but he's going to a clinic in America where they can treat brain injured children in a very remarkable way.'

She ignored my remark. Carol began to find out what Doran

could do. It appeared to be the usual list of what Doran couldn't do.

'Do you think he's ready to sit up yet?' She looked at the doctor. 'Shall we get him measured for a corner seat?'

I couldn't conceive of what she meant by a 'corner seat' but I knew that the only way Doran could sit in a car was to be forced into it by the safety harness. There was no means by which Carol could induce his body to bend.

I said, 'I think he should concentrate on crawling.'

Carol looked at the doctor who said, 'If you come here for physiotherapy I expect you to accept our methods of treatment.' She must have seen me looking dubious, because she went on, 'I know the place you mentioned and I think it right to tell you now that you'll be wasting your money if you go there.'

'I think you're very lucky to live so near to us,' said Carol. 'It's far the best place for children like Doran.'

The doctor smiled. 'We'd like to have him here,' she said.

I looked from one to the other and back to Doran.

'Can you reorganize Doran's brain so that another part can take over?'

'I'm afraid Glenn Doman is entirely wrong; the brain doesn't work like that,' the doctor replied firmly. 'I'm not going to give you false hopes.'

The calipers seemed to move from their corner and take a step towards me. I snarled back at them. Then I met the doctor's eyes.

'If you decide to go to America,' she said steadily, 'you could be doing your son positive harm. I think Glenn Doman's methods are highly dangerous, and I'm afraid once you make that decision we cannot treat Doran here.'

I was aware that the programme of work proposed by the Institutes would leave no time to make even social visits to physiotherapy.

'I've some time to make up my mind. Where we do seem to have common ground is the question of swimming.'

She was prepared to concede that we could use the hydro-therapy pool. The warmer water would mean that Doran could move more easily. We were on probation. If our activity disturbed the other children it would have to stop.

'The other children?' I queried.

'We take a class from the school there,' said Carol. 'They're quite severe cases, so they need a lot of help.'

It was possible to go up to the pool at once and get ready. My costume was in the car, Lili could swim in her pants, but Doran still didn't actually have a bathing costume. We were ahead of the class and changed quickly, the water looked warm and inviting. Lili chose a rubber ring from an enormous heap of coloured inflatables lying along the side, and we climbed in. I could feel Doran relax as the temperature rose around him. I looked back to make sure Lili was safe; she was already half hidden by a bobbing mass of inflatables.

'Doesn't Doran want one?' she asked.

'They'd be more of an incentive for him to look at, Lili. Push them ahead of him.'

She paddled over with a selection of rings in tow. While I was disengaging them from Doran and trying to persuade Lili that I meant him to look at the inflatables from a distance, the class began to be carried in.

Once the children's bodies had been adequately supported by numerous tyres and floats, they were pushed off and began their slow journey towards us down the pool. I was waiting for them to surround us, when one of the 'physios' blew a whistle and cried, 'Clear the water. Everybody out!'

It was the quickest swimming lesson I'd ever witnessed. I went on pulling Doran through the little waves, when another physio called, 'I'd get out quickly if I were you; we're going to drain the pool.'

This seemed to be a peculiar thing to be doing. I decided to accept it with good grace. We climbed out, and I began to dry Doran in the cubicle, while Lili went to say 'hello' to the other children. She came back enthusiastically, 'Mummy, someone did a big pooh in the pool.'

Doran was smiling; he looked very pink and clean and happy.

'It's a little boy called Jamie,' she said. 'He did it before, so they won't let him in the water again.'

'That seems rather hard,' I said.

The physio pulled back the curtains and began to apologize profusely. 'The children have one chance,' she said. 'It's a pity but it must have been Jamie.'

'Did he say he did it?'

'He can't speak.'

'Where was it?'

'Quite near you, I'm afraid.'

Doran couldn't speak either. I looked into his happy smiling face and recalled the relaxing properties of warm water.

'It's unlikely that it was Jamie,' I said.

'Why?'

'Because I think it was Doran.'

'Oh, but it was much too big for a baby.'

'That about sums it up,' I said. 'It was Doran. Doran eats ravenously, grows minimally and excretes extravagantly.'

Her eyes fixed on me.

'I'm sorry,' I said meekly. 'And I'm very sorry about Jamie. Will we get a second chance?'

'I should think so, but I can't think how it got out of his bathing trunks.'

The usefulness of bathing trunks dawned suddenly upon me. We got our second chance, but thereafter, regardless of an element of sensory deprivation, Doran always wore a pair of plastic pants, plus a tight fitting bathing costume when I took him swimming. It took Lili a year to forget the incident.

The visit was living proof of the urgency of treating Doran sooner rather than later. I had read in *What To Do About Your Brain Injured Child* that in order to teach children to crawl, it was necessary to 'pattern' the right information into them. One did this by manipulating their arms, legs and head in a rhythmical crawling movement for five minute periods. This made good sense but it needed three people to accomplish. Ultimately I discovered a precrawling patterning which only involved two people. The child lay face downwards, and while

85

one person turned his head from side to side the other gently rocked the child's body by lifting first his right arm and leg, and then his left arm and leg alternately for five minutes.

The following morning we were having breakfast on the floor. Doran lay like a fish out of water consumed with indignation and immobility. It was time to take a further step up the evolutionary ladder. As soon as we'd finished eating we were going to pattern him. I explained the situation to Lili; Doran was in no frame of mind to hear. Then, kneeling beside him, I began to lift an arm and a leg in turn, and tip his trunk. Lili was naturally anxious to be as involved as possible, and offered to 'do' her brother's head.

The first patterning, if it could be credited as such, was a slapstick affair which the subject found riotously amusing. I decided that if he were to make any long term gains Lili should, at least for the moment, switch her attention to a doll. My alternative was to call Judith and request another pair of hands. The number was engaged, at least I knew she was up. I put the receiver down.

I could hear Doran yelling and laughing, Lili was evidently patterning him again. Before I could separate them the phone rang.

'Hello . . . Lili, leave Doran alone!' I shouted partly down the receiver and partly across the room.

'You're fortunate it's me,' said the voice on the other end of the line. 'I've been trying to call you.'

'Judith! Do you want to listen to me first, or shall I listen to you.'

'Listen . . . Dianna's here already. Come for lunch and we'll drive over and see her this afternoon.'

The noise from the kitchen was intensifying.

'That's perfect, see you at lunch. Oh and thank you.'

'What did you say?'

'Thank you, Judith. I love you. Goodbye.'

I hung up and rushed back to my abandoned children. Lili had gone, so had Doran. Was he suddenly crawling, or had I had some aberration and forgotten where I'd left him?

'Look, Mummy!'

Lili came trotting out of the bathroom with Doran's feet in her hands. As a result, the rest of Doran was dragged, stomach down, across the floor. When his face came into view I saw a grin of incredulous delight was spreading from ear to ear.

'Doran's crawling now,' she said, and proceeded to bounce him happily towards the living room. I chased after them.

'Lili! You have the right spirit – now give him back immediately.'

It took rather longer than usual to arrive at the baths that morning.

We reached Judith's to find she had cooked something very special for lunch. Each mouthful drew me closer to meeting Dianna. Judith began telling me more about her; but it was impossible for me to listen to any description when I was so near to the actual person.

Dianna's house finally appeared, the door opened and I was suddenly facing a woman of considerable and unexpected elegance. She wore a softly tailored suit and her fair hair was swept up and fixed with a single lily. She didn't look as if she could possibly let a child near her.

I rolled up the sleeve of my rather bedraggled blouse, and held out my hand to her. She hugged me, hugged Doran, spontaneously removed him from my arms and put him on the floor. Then she proceeded to disappear on to the floor herself. I had never seen a perfectly sober young woman, apparently dressed to go to a wedding, stretch out on the floor and begin crawling as if she were in a civil defence class.

'Come on, Doran,' she said. 'Let's see what you can do.'

The lily remained unruffled. Her crawling was superb. Doran watched, and began to laugh.

Judith said, 'Looks good.'

Dianna studied Doran.

'Does he like being down there?'

'Yes,' I said. 'You've just paid him a great compliment.'

'Imitation is the sincerest form of flattery, huh?'

'You have a fantastic style,' I said. 'I shall be pleased when he's imitating you.'

Judith said, 'He generally screams his head off.'

Dianna crawled over to Doran.

'It'll grow on you,' she said.

By this time Judith and I were lying on the floor too. We continued our conversation with our heads propped up on our elbows. Lili caught sight of the garden outside and the edge of a sandpit with buckets and spades peeping out.

Dianna was full of energy and enthusiasm. She could understand that although we'd been living close to many edges we'd never lost direction.

'The Institutes sounds like my natural home,' I said.

Dianna agreed. 'You kids are going to have a lot of fun.'

She then proceeded to describe all the things we would be doing in a day.

Judith said, 'Okay, so when does she go to the bathroom?'

'I won't drink, there'll be no time.'

Dianna laughed, 'But you do have to be very healthy; you look a little thin. What do you eat?'

Judith had a swift answer. 'She eats lettuce.'

I protested that I ate bread, peanut butter and lettuce; and I rolled up my sleeves to show my muscles. After some argument it was decided to let the matter of diet rest.

Dianna turned her attention to Doran's eyesight. For this he left the floor briefly while she popped him into her own broom cupboard and shone a torch into his eyes.

'He has a light reflex. Let's work on it,' she said. 'Make him some black and white optical paintings that really stretch his vision. Put them everywhere.'

Then she produced three large pieces of card with large letters printed on them. 'Doran, I have a special treat, we're going to look at some words.' She read each card very clearly and flashed it with the skill of a poker player.

'"Mummy". "Lili". "Doran". Good boy, did you like it?'

'Could he see that?' asked Judith.

'Come on now,' I said, 'he lifted his head higher for those cards than he usually does for his dinner.'

Dianna nodded. 'Kids like learning better than eating.'

'I'd still say you can learn a lot from a good dinner,' said Judith, whose intellect also went into her cooking.

I touched her arm, 'Don't worry. His reading will teach him to pay your food unusual compliments.'

'The best kind he can pay me, is to eat it.'

Dianna suggested a compromise. In the cause of stimulating Doran's brain we should develop his sense of taste and smell by giving him contrasting titbits and odours.

'Lili would love that,' I said.

'Absolutely. This all includes Lili. Now we'll take some photographs and you can send them to Glenn with your letter. Let's find Lili.'

Lili was building a sand castle for a prince and princess. Dianna showed her a Polaroid camera.

'Do you want to see some magic? Will you and Doran be Indian hunters and crawl up to the house for me? I'll take your photograph here, and by the time you reach the door you can see it.'

To persuade Lili that crawling as an Indian hunter didn't entail towing Doran by the heels, meant that I had to become one myself. Diana snapped us.

'That's great work,' she applauded. 'Now here's your photo.'

'Mummy, it's magic, we're changing colour!' The photo darkened and three figures emerged from the grass.

'That,' said Judith, 'is the first record of your new life.'

Dianna took some more photos and sent me off to write the letter. We reviewed it, included the pictures and put it in an envelope. As I wrote the address Dianna said, 'I can see by your face you're already in Philadelphia.'

'I shall work as though I am. I want to start patterning Doran.'

I instructed Judith while Lili and Dianna patterned a doll (which like the buckets and spades and sandpit, belonged to the family from whom she was renting the flat).

We moved Doran as harmoniously as we could. Catching intermittent glimpses of his mouth, as it turned from side to side, I could see that it's corners were up.

The doll had a rather stiff neck.

'He likes it Judith! How often can you help? It needs to be four patternings a day, minimum.'

'While we're here you have only to ask, but . . .'

'But?'

'We have to go back to the States next month. I have a music course at Bennington.'

'I'd forgotten, but we can still make a good start if we come to you on the way to the baths and on the way home.'

'Come for breakfast; we'll sandwich breakfast between Doran's patternings.'

Dianna had a very busy schedule before she left and I didn't know when I would see her again. She had given me confidence. I knew I would be using my time in the best possible way while I was waiting for an appointment at the Institutes.

I produced some large black and white optical paintings and fixed them everywhere, including the back of the passenger seat of the car, so that Doran stared straight at them when we were driving. I also put a different picture on the back of the adjacent seat for Lili. The idea seemed very appealing; car seats are boring to look at, and the landscape outside is not always of consuming interest. Lili lived part of the journey in her paintings. I could hear her talking earnestly to their characters and I hoped Doran was equally riveted by the white triangle on the black ground, and the black circle on the white ground.

We continued visiting the hospital for the warm baths. It was now perfectly possible for me to accept the physiotherapists there as kindly well-intentioned people. They were locked, like characters, into a tragic play, from which they could not be transposed. We were free, we could come and go; not so the other children.

The doctor there remained adamant about the Institutes. Her argument was now more oblique than direct. She spoke firmly about the 'right' thing to do, which was always directly opposite from the thing I was planning. I desperately wished I could see every child in the place thrown out of its wheel chair and crawling down the long convenient corridors. The only subject that was getting uncomfortable was that of Doran's eyes. She wanted me to see an eye specialist with a view to an operation. Since I had no intention at all of letting a surgeon interfere with a symptom of brain injury, while he ignored its cause, I made various excuses. I forgot appointments. Unless it came to a show down, and we lost the pool, I would be forced to put in at least a nominal appearance at the hospital. When our next appointment arrived we were there punctually, and looking cooperative.

The doctor gave Doran a nominal examination and said: 'The problem is due to the broad canthus of the eyes. The bone is probably pressing on a nerve.'

'What about the brain injury?'

'It has nothing to do with the brain injury.'

'What?'

'It's a separate problem.'

'But isn't it rather strange that before he was injured his eyes looked perfectly straight?'

'That doesn't necessarily have any connection.'

'But I thought visual problems were often symptomatic of brain injury.'

The eye specialist sighed.

'Look,' he said, 'I cannot examine him any further this morning. Take these drops and put them into his eye three times a day for the next week, and then we'll have another appointment.'

'What do they do?'

'They dilate the pupils so that I can examine him more closely.'

'Do they affect his vision?'

'It will be a little blurred.'

'But Doran's vision's already like that.'

'It won't worry him, I assure you.'

'How do you know?' I asked. 'There is no way you could know.'

'If you want me to examine his eyes properly you must give him the drops.'

'Doran is just beginning to make some visual sense of the world and you're asking me to deliberately upset it.'

'I think that is too strong a reaction. You have a responsibility towards your child. I suggest you think about it more seriously.'

'Thank you,' I said, 'I do feel very responsible for Doran. If you give me the drops I'll phone up and make an appointment when I've given the matter some thought.'

He smiled. 'I'm sure you will appreciate how important this is to your son.'

I disengaged Lili from the curtains, which she was quietly twisting into a swing and, lifting Doran high in my arms, we departed with good grace.

As we reached the main corridor I began turning the interview over in my mind. I had the profoundest sense that I was being caught. I was aware that nothing in particular could actually be done about Doran's eyes unless it was accepted that the hurt eyes were a symptom of the damaged brain. The drops were a contradiction of all I was doing to stimulate Doran's eyesight. There was no doubt in my mind that sight meant something to him now. (I kept expanding and changing a stack of reading cards in the car, and showed them to Doran and Lili whenever we got in or out.) As we passed the last waste-paper bin I knew I couldn't give them to him and I didn't want to think about it again. I let go of Lili's hand, reached into my pocket and tossed the little bottle away.

'What was that, Mummy?'

'An inspired but irresponsible gesture, Lili. Do you want scrambled egg or cheese on toast for tea?'

The patterning went well, so did tasting and smelling. I carried a group of matchboxes filled with the day's examples and produced them with great flamboyance. Lili took it very seriously. Then Judith's departure made it essential to find alternative help. The best plan was to visit my parents on the Isle of Wight; Doran was fit enough to travel and Lili wanted a more predictable adventure. Moe accepted an invitation to come with us. This was vital because of the number of things which needed to be carried. Carrying things put another rather different strain on my body; as I worried less about Doran, I was beginning to develop an uneasy feeling about myself. If I was going to be ill, it was better sooner, rather than later. I felt as if part of my body were torn, or still tearing, as a result of Doran's birth; and the sensation was increased if I lifted anything without due care. I had hoped that if I ignored the problem it would eventually go away, because there simply wasn't room in my head for any further anxiety. Going home to my parents encouraged the innocent belief that it was safe to be ill because there was somebody to look after me. It also put me in mind of the troubles of my grandmother after my mother's birth. I remembered being told she had to wear a ring inside her to stop her uterus falling out; I had been awe-inspired by a life of such daily discomfort, and relieved to think of it as an old-fashioned complaint.

Moe met us at the station. Both children were very excited and we were delighted that the train was on time. I opened a door and carried Lili into the compartment. The other passengers were friendly businessmen on their way home from the City. They welcomed Lili's smiling face and tucked her in a corner while I went back for the rest of the luggage. I stepped down and reached out for a suitcase, but Moe suggested I take Doran. Without any warning at all, the train started to pull out of the station, with Lili's smiling face still at the window.

Then almost unbelievably, while the train was still moving, the carriage door opened, and a man in a bowler hat lowered Lili onto the edge of the platform. The carriages were running by, just above her face. If she moved an inch, she'd be under them. I screamed. It sounded primitive but it stopped the train.

By now the windows of the carriages were all open and the guard and the engine driver were on the platform. Lili hadn't moved an inch.

I picked her up in my arms aware that everyone was asking everyone else what had happened, or offering explanations as to why it had happened.

'Lili, you were very, very brave,' I said. I was still wondering how she had managed to remain alive.

'We're all right,' I said, 'only, never let that happen to anyone again.'

We walked up the train to the section that was going to Portsmouth and climbed into a compartment. It was, by chance, the same compartment. I could see the man in the bowler hat; he was white and shaking. I heard him say, 'I don't understand why I did it, I tried to put her down very carefully.'

Lili was unperturbed and asked, 'Could we have our picnic?'

The rest of the journey was as uneventful as it is possible to be with two lively children. Doran's main method of showing any emotion was to jerk his head back unexpectedly and give you a stunning blow on the jaw. At the same time his feet shot out pushing any plates, cups or other delicate objects that might happen to be in their way onto the floor.

My father met us off the ferry. He was naturally apprehensive about meeting Doran. Doran, on the contrary, wasn't at all worried about meeting his grandfather. He transmitted this by a beaming smile whenever he caught sight of him. Before the first evening was up, they were both down on the kitchen floor. My father had pulled out most of the pots and pans and, with Doran's obvious approval, he was banging them seriously on the linoleum. Besides my parents, there was my great aunt. She was eighty-nine years older than Doran but they shared the same sense of humour and bubbling infectious laughter. The only elements in the house not to rejoice in Doran's presence were the cats. They took refuge under my parents bed and sulked shamelessly.

My mother had arranged for us to go swimming twice a day, once in a hydrotherapy pool and once at a holiday camp. To this we could now add four patternings a day, and the floor programme. At the end of a fortnight Doran was holding his head off the floor, and eager to get at the pots and pans. My mother's interest had switched to my health. It was true that I was going off to pee with ever increasing frequency, and that although I was thin, my stomach was far from flat. She was courageous enough to make such personal comments and risk the terrible consequences of my indignation. It was hard to be too indignant because what she pointed out was fact. I said, 'Grandmother's footsteps. I think I'm following in my grandmother's footsteps. What was it she had?'

'A prolapse.'

'I have the feeling that I'm coming to pieces in strategic areas.'

My mother wasted no time in making me an appointment with the family doctor. He was surprised; I had a considerable and inconvenient prolapse. The only answer to it was surgery, unless I wanted a ring fitted, which I immediately refused. I fondly imagined that surgery meant a few stitches and an overnight stay in hospital. It did not. The amount of sewing required was more in the region of a highly skilled, two hour job, in short, a major operation necessitating two weeks in hospital, and two months' rest to ensure that scar tissue had healed. Besides this, the waiting list for operations which had anything to do with 'women's complaints' was renowned for its length; I might have to wait a year, maybe more.

'But I can't wait,' I cried. 'I'm going to America and it's vital for Doran, so there must be a way.'

We went home to discuss the situation. The problems were numerous. Firstly, I didn't know exactly when I was going to America; secondly, who was going to look after Doran and Lili? My mother wanted to, but, although coming up for a late retirement, she was still a teacher and the breadwinner, while Doran, as everyone at home had now discovered, didn't have peaceful nights. Perhaps Lili could stay with my parents and Doran stay with Judith? I couldn't imagine Doran in any household as an independent guest. Should I go into hospital on the Island or try the various hospitals I knew so well in Sussex? Would *any* hospital take me early enough? If it didn't, and I planned to go ahead, it meant accepting the compromise of having a ring fitted until I could have surgery. I would be as my grandmother before me.

The issues became more and more complex and confused. If Doran was with Judith, and I was in hospital in Sussex, I could see him, but not Lili. But would it make matters worse for Judith, if he did see me? Then I remembered that if I was in hospital, Doran couldn't go on being breastfed; I would have to wean him.

We were to stay on the Island for a few more days, after which Moe was due to start work as a librarian. While taking our ritual swim in the holiday camp pool, one of the residents asked me if we were coming back for Christmas. I was just beginning to answer that if the pool was open, we'd in all probability still be swimming in it, when something very obvious struck me. It was so clear that I paddled Doran over to Moe and said, 'Where's the place you'd least like to be at Christmas?'

'I'm not sure. Prison? Hospital? Under Waterloo Bridge?'

'You wouldn't *choose* to be in any of those places?'

'Would *you* spend Christmas under Waterloo Bridge?'

'No, but I'd spend it in the hospital.'

'You did that last year.'

'Exactly, and everybody who could, went home. No one is going to want to have a major operation on Christmas Eve if they have the choice – nobody but me!'

'Linda!'

'No, really, it's superb. I'm bound to get it done before the New Year, besides I actually like hospitals at Christmas.'

We continued pushing Doran between us like a small boat.

Moe said, 'I'm not doing anything at Christmas, Linda. I could come and look after Doran and Lili too.'

'Do you really mean that. You of all people know what it's like. It would be absolutely wonderful – but is it realistic?'

'Of course, you do it all the time. I'd like to.'

I caught up with Doran and hugged him, and then moved on to hug Moe.

'Why are you always there when I need you?'

'It would be a cliché to say that's what friends are for.'

Our doctor was both amused and delighted, and phoned the consultant. I would have to wait a month for an appointment but the prospect looked hopeful. I continued to walk on the invisible grass of Philadelphia.

My mother came home with us because Moe had to return to London. I was determined to go on patterning Doran and spent the evening listing people who might possibly help. I could see how vital the frequency of the patterning must be, and once Doran had tasted it, there was no way I could let him backtrack. My mother suddenly said, 'Why not ask Margaret?'

Margaret was my next door neighbour. Out of respect for privacy I hadn't considered asking someone so close. That evening, when Lili was in bed, my mother went next door. She came back rather merry on two large glasses of sherry and the news that Margaret would pattern Doran at eight-thirty every morning and five-thirty every evening. Margaret was instantly canonized.

The following morning, as soon as the smell of bacon and eggs had drifted away from Margaret's window and into mine, she was there, catching up with the ghost of her breakfast and ready to work. Doran fitted comfortably on the end of the big kitchen table, which had come a long way since it was found supporting fruit and vegetables outside a greengrocer's shop in North London. Lili ate watchfully at the other end. Doran was perfectly happy with this experience. I knew that I had enough friends who would pattern him at other times during the day, the sun was streaming in, and the immediate future seemed secure. When Margaret left, I took Doran on my knee for a moment to reward him for his good humour. It was Sunday and my mother had planned to leave in the afternoon after we'd been swimming. Doran suddenly wriggled. If he could have moved as he would have liked, he would have probably landed on Lili's knee. But Doran could only manage one way, his spine arched, his head went back and sank with some force into my front teeth. I heard a shattering sound. I knew what had happened, but for a moment I elected not to take it in. There was a mirror hanging just above the table. Cautiously I focused on my mouth. The left hand front tooth was in bits and pieces on my tongue. Ten years previously it would have been the most tragic disaster I could think of. I spat out the remaining fragments and pursed my lips.

'I think I need a dentist.'

Lili said, 'Never mind, mummy, grannie will put it back for you.'

'That's a lovely thought, Lili, but it may take her some time.'

I stood up and looked squarely in the mirror and sat down again and started to laugh. It was funny laughter because my breath seemed to whistle through the gap. I didn't mind.

My mother put her arms round me.

'Heaven has a lovely sense of humour,' I said. 'Do you think the price of getting to Philadelphia was this front tooth?'

My mother continued to hug me. 'No, it seems rather unfortunate,' she said. 'Will the dentist see you on a Sunday, darling?'

7

I VISITED FRIENDS who would pattern Doran. Almost always, they had children of their own; sometimes of Doran's age. The contrast between normal development and the child they were helping was very clear. I couldn't be sure how much they believed in what they were doing, but no one tried to undermine my confidence in it. We lived between the bath, the floor and a convenient table.

Lili particularly liked calling at a small farm, hidden away up on the forest. There were hens and ducks, and curious pigs with red-gold hair. A young graduate called Brenda was temporarily employed to look after these pigs and the small holding. She was always willing to put down the slop bucket to turn Doran's head, while Lili took grain up to the hens. The more we talked about the Institutes, the more Brenda became intrigued by it. Every so often she would say, 'I can't believe it, Linda, it seems like a dream', and I'd assure her it wasn't. Until one day, she announced her intention of foresaking the pigs and going to work at the Institutes. 'But perhaps I could stay and help Doran first; he'll be needing it,' she said. We agreed that Brenda would come to America, and then remain with us and share the job of healing.

I watched the subject of all our plans in close combat with the floor. There was no doubt in my mind who was going to win. Doran's nose had ceased to be buried in the carpet. If he brought down his fists vehemently, he could jam things between the knuckles. It was clear that whatever he saw, he could make sense out of it.

I developed an intelligence programme for him which started

at five-thirty a.m., when Doran was very much awake. We propped up a Ladybird picture book and pulled out a box full of objects, which corresponded with each picture. If there was a picture of a spoon I would put a spoon in his hand, give him as much tactile and visual information about it as possible, and then pass on to the next item.

One morning Lili rushed back from the letter box with a reply from the Institutes. It was brimming with information and indicated that the final date for the evaluation would be February or March. In September Judith returned in time for Doran's first birthday. She was impressed with what she saw.

'Six teeth Doran – how could you be so normal?'

'They have their eccentricity, Judith; they're like spikes. He missed out on the last coating of calcium.'

'Does he bite?'

'Now he has teeth he thinks nature intends him to eat me rather than suck.'

'Does he want steak or cake for the great day?'

Judith baked, and directed a birthday party. Not long after this he did the most amazing thing – he rolled onto his back.

Once there, he was stuck like a turtle, but the event was cause for jubilation. My own ability to celebrate anything was becoming inhibited by the prolapse. I couldn't dance or even sneeze without the uncomfortable recognition that in a very real way I was falling apart.

By the beginning of November, Doran could lie on his side and wriggle into an upturned box. He expected to see changes in himself. We spent the evenings playing games before the fire. The floor was a landscape of our intelligence programme. By 10.30 p.m. my phrases of encouragement were less intelligible and I found myself dozing off with my head cushioned on a heap of dolls. It was at this hour that Brenda often appeared. She seemed to carry us all up to bed and the last noise I could hear would be that of her vacuuming the floor.

When Brenda didn't relieve us, Doran eventually allowed himself to be tucked up with Lili. Once her head was safely on the pillow he sighed and closed his eyes. I resurrected the house and then slid in between them. My own sleep should have been disturbed by the pressure of raising £1,000 but it wasn't.

The time had nevertheless come to take fund raising seriously. Judy proposed we hold council at her house, and invite Bert, Brenda, Judy and Peter.

After discussing the more colourful ways of raising money we came down in favour of a series of jumble sales and a lot of publicity. Bert was a rich source of practical information; she foresaw problems and we thrashed our way through them.

The more help we could get, the better it would be, so I decided to phone a woman who'd been my support councillor, in the National Child Birth Trust. Before I had got very far with my story I realized my mistake.

'You have to face it that Doran will never be well and that if you go ahead with your scheme you will be a parasite on the community . . .'

'But . . .'

'I'm sorry, Linda; that's my final word . . .'

It was not her final word. I had unleashed something in her that impelled her verbally onwards until I was forced to hang up.

Bert said, 'You'll have to expect that sort of thing, Linda; you're sticking your neck out.'

Brenda said, 'I don't think many people would behave like that.'

We argued a little about human nature which seemed to be either elusive or contradictory. Bert pointed out the time.

It was decided to have two jumble sales, one just before Christmas and one just afterwards. Judith returned to the subject of my health; she was more aware than I was of the stress of surgery and its aftermath.

'When you come out of hospital you're coming to stay with us. No children, you need rest. Your parents and Moe can manage Doran and Lili.' Since fitness was crucial I accepted being affectionately bullied into this unexpected holiday by everyone at once.

'They'll survive without you, you know.'

'But will I survive without them?'

By some miracle the Village Hall was free the Saturday before Christmas. My friends began to phone up to ask where they could deliver jumble. It arrived at various points in town and a lot of it arrived at the cottage. Bert decided we ought to throw in a group of my paintings: they would at least make the hall look more attractive. Once we began to raise money we would need a bank account to put it in. One child did not constitute a charity but we could open a Benevolent Fund with Judith, Bert and myself as trustees.

Another friend suggested I write a piece for *Woman's Own*. The idea was accepted, but I still wondered when I would find the time. Judith said, 'What else are you going to do in hospital, knit?'

'I can't knit. I thought of reading Tolstoy but I'll write instead.'

'You need the money. My apologies to Tolstoy but other people's literature can wait.'

It was nearly a year since Doran had been taken to hospital with kidney failure. I had recently changed my doctor and hoped it would be a good omen. Both children had slight colds but Lili's became worse and her temperature flew up and down. Our doctor diagnosed a throat infection and prescribed antibiotic and junior aspirin. Lili couldn't eat or talk, then for a while she seemed to be recovering. She lay on the sofa with her crayons and colouring book.

I spent the night listening to her breathing; towards the morning it grew shallower and sharper. She wasn't interested in waking up. Her eyelashes were clogged with catarrh and curled back stiffly. She had the beauty of a newborn child, and a grown woman. I didn't want to see her life rolled into this one moment; she needed help quickly. The doctor was out on call but his wife thought she could trace him, and ask him to come immediately. After a moment's hesitation I phoned Brenda. Someone else must have fed the pigs because in less than fifteen minutes she was with me; she took Doran downstairs and gave him breakfast while I stayed beside Lili.

She stirred and opened her eyes; they were peaceful but so very far away. I went on talking to her until our doctor arrived. His reactions were very quick. 'She has pneumonia. Which hospital?'

'Brighton.'

'That's where Doran went on his way to Guy's, isn't it?'

'Yes.'

'They'll remember you. Can you take her right away?'

I nodded. He dialled the number and got through to admissions.

'They are expecting you. Remember she's in no immediate danger, drive carefully.'

Brenda drove and Doran sat calmly in his car seat. Lili was lying across my lap. I didn't want her to sleep so although I was shaking myself, I shook her still more. I shouted nursery rhymes in her ears.

The day was dark and overcast. After a while it began to rain. As we reached the coast, the traffic built up. Since neither of us knew the way to the hospital we were forced to stop at a garage and enquire. Brenda repeated the directions over again. As visibility decreased, she said: 'Do you think we turn up here?'

The car skidded violently. A wall flashed by, we slithered round a bend and confronted a hill. We were on the wrong side of the road with our front wheels on the pavement. Doran yelled angrily. Lili opened her eyes a little wider and I said, placidly, 'Have we lost a wheel, Brenda?' She climbed out.

'No, it's oil all over the road.'

Another car began skidding behind us. It lurched to a standstill a few feet away. Brenda leapt back. She restarted the car. It slipped and slithered to the first available turning. We threaded through a network of back streets and then, a little way ahead, I recognized the identical entrance we'd passed through with Doran as the emergency, almost exactly the year before.

'We've won – turn – over there.'

She overshot, braked and reversed into the car park.

A nurse welcomed us. 'Did you miss the chaos?' she asked. 'Radio Brighton just warned cars off the ring road. A tanker's been leaking rivers of oil the full length of it.'

The admissions room was snug and warm. The doctor greeted us effusively, 'Don't worry, we can cope with this one here.'

In an hour Lili was in an oxygen tent with a saline drip in her arm; she looked immeasurably brighter.

'Lili,' I said, 'you are a princess with a glass coach and you can drink rosewater through your wrist.'

She looked admiringly at the narrow tube which disappeared into her skin. 'Where's Doran?'

'Doran's gone to Judith's. Brenda took him. He's having a holiday and I'm staying with you.'

'Good.'

The room was hot, and since she had a temperature no one had bothered her with night things. Nurses kept popping in to admire her body as if it were a well known Renaissance painting.

At first I spent the night sleeping on the edge of Lili's bed. Later, when she alighted from her glass coach and relinquished the unorthodox way of drinking, we slept with our arms round each other in the bed which was intended to be mine.

A physiotherapist came in three times a day to loosen her choked lungs by means of pit-a-pats. This meant beating Lili's chest and back, lightly with the finger tips. Lili was charmed by the word but not the action. However, they were an extremely effective method of clearing lungs.

My daily trips to the toy library took me through another ward in which there were several brain injured children who seemed to be admitted for mysterious complaints. Amongst so many cheerful young patients, they were the only lonely ones.

When Lili had a nap during the day, telephone calls from the front line of our Benevolent Fund instructed me to make posters for the jumble sale. If I asked Judith how she was coping with Doran, I couldn't get past the reply. 'Just fine' at which point the subject was switched firmly back to Lili.

We had been away nearly a week when Lili asked, 'Where's Doran? I want to see Doran.'

Her lungs were clear. Her eyes were full of mischief. It was time to go home.

The hospital car arrived after lunch. It was cold but there were no reports of snow or ice. I was assured that it had just been serviced. We were to share part of the journey. A mother climbed in beside us with her child; the boy looked about four years old – he was handsome but limp. He smiled silently up at her.

'They don't understand him,' she said, looking back at the hospital.

I nursed Lili gently, while she continued, 'People don't know what it's like to have a child like this; they don't expect you to love him.'

'I do.'

'What was wrong with your little girl?'

'Pneumonia, but she's better now.'

'She's pretty isn't she?' She turned to Lili.

'Your father will be glad to see you when you get home.'

Lili was half asleep and didn't reply. The car drew up and the woman lifted her son out. 'I may see you again,' she said.

Brenda had been staying at the cottage to keep it warm; she was there to welcome us. The fire was glowing and she'd baked some bread which made the air smell sweet. Boxes of sorted and unsorted jumble stood round the walls. We were two days off the big sale. She tucked Lili up on the sofa and gave her a plate of warm bread spread with melting butter and honey. Then she handed me a mug of tea.

'You had a letter this morning. It's a bit muddy.' She had stepped on it on her way back from feeding the pigs.

'It's my hospital appointment; I'm due there at 4 p.m. on 23 December.'

'You're all set then?'

'We're all set. I shall be well, we'll have our evaluation fixed and we'll take Doran to Philadelphia, won't we, Lili?'

'I'd do anything for you,' Lili sang huskily; it was the song we sang to each other when we thought of the future. Brenda picked it up and went on—

'For you, dear, anything – for you mean everything to me.'

We put our arms round each other:

'I'd go anywhere for you, dear – anywhere . . .'

The door opened and Judith came in carrying Doran. 'You kids give one a great welcome!'

'He looks bonny,' said Brenda.

'He should be; he's been eating three course meals and sucking on avocados.'

Doran smiled broadly in acknowledgement. He was brought round to be hugged and then lowered onto the floor near the fire. He promptly rolled over, paused, and then flexing the muscles of his side, he rolled back onto his stomach, as if it were the easiest most desirable act in the world.

'It's the surprise he had for you,' said Judith.

Doran continued to roll; he saw no reason for modesty.

Lili climbed off the sofa and yelled hoarsely, 'Doran, roll over to me, come on, Doran!'

Doran obliged. He spent the entire evening showing off.

The following afternoon the first of the local reporters arrived with her photographer. Doran was now in command of the carpet. He had rotated himself to and fro all day. Seeing the visitors renewed his zeal and he gave no indication of the limitations of his mobility.

'Is this Doran?' enquired the reporter. 'I thought he was paralysed.'

'He looks very well to me,' rejoined the photographer.

I debated whether or not I should hold Doran down with my foot, when Judith arrived; she had predicted the situation earlier and waved a handful of photographs.

'Do you want to see what a child like Doran should be doing? This kid was born on the same day.'

The photos showed a small boy running, climbing and kicking a ball. They all looked back at Doran. I said, 'I think you mistook enthusiasm for ability. Doran is one and a half years old, but all he can do is roll from left to right after a lot of patterning.'

'Patterning?'

I explained what I'd learned. Light suddenly began to dawn in their eyes.

A team from the alternative local paper arrived the following morning. Doran was actually tired from his new form of transportation; he slouched appropriately in my arms. From now on Doran's disabilities had to be sung out loud. We had to prove the need for treatment and to demonstrate that it worked. We were having lunch at Judith's, the day the papers came out. The headline read:

'HOPE FOR TRAGIC DORAN'

My Athertoid infant had just put away a whole fillet of plaice with sautéed rice and vegetables, and was rolling buoyantly under the chair.

'The kid doesn't look tragic enough,' said Judith.

'Doran may not be Prince Hamlet, Judith, but he's no attendant Lord either.'

Michael said, 'Nothing could convince Doran he was help-less.'

'He's a hero,' said Lili.

My son was grooming us for the roles of our lives.

The following Saturday was the day of the jumble sale. Doran, Lili and I were instructed to stay at home and keep warm and calm. My paintings were sent as viceroys. Lili found the denuding of the house painful; the boxes looked intriguingly like Christmas presents.

'Will Father Christmas know we've gone to granny's, mummy?' she repeated anxiously.

At last I heard cars in the lane; Judith and Bert were back. They were talking and joking in the heightened emotional state of people who have been through a war and come out alive. Bert said, 'Well we can't say "never again", but it was a nerve-wracking experience. How much did we make?'

'Over £70 since I started counting.'

'You can't say that's bad, Judith – not considering we're bringing back enough for another sale.'

People had turned up with so many extra contributions we had no alternative but to repeat the affray as soon as possible. They were already planning where, and how, and giving me instructions not to worry about any single thing that came into my head.

If I didn't know what I was letting myself in for, everyone else did. Brenda was going to continue to live at the cottage, keep it warm and forward my mail. (I still needed to have one more letter from the Institutes, finalizing the date of Doran's evaluation.) The next great landmark on our road, would be my safe arrival at the hospital. Once I was securely immobilized in a bed, the rest of the family could be delivered to the Fairy Grotto now standing on the site of my parents' house. Moe and my great aunt would be there under the tinsel, warming up mince pies . . . I had deliberately left travelling until the last possible connection. We started out with time to spare for crossing the pedestrian bridge onto the adjacent platform. As we passed the village shop, Lili decided she wanted some grapes. Brenda pulled in obligingly. When she tried to restart, the ignition key broke off in the ignition. There was no way we could get it out.

'This isn't true, is it, Linda?'

'My life appears to be some sort of initiative test. Shall I phone for a taxi?'

'It'll take too long. Let me get my car.'

We were near enough to the farm for this to be feasible. The only problem was that I had estimated the timing with the throttle of my vehicle in mind. Brenda's car had a maximum speed of thirty miles an hour. She drove with her foot pressed flat on the accelerator. We didn't talk, we simply willed the car to move. Everything went by in a kind of dreamlike slow motion. Had we been running on my pulse, we would have burned up the road to Crawley.

The car arrived at its infuriatingly legal pace. The station clock gave the thumbs down but I knew the train was often late. I induced our party to continue running.

'Did the Portsmouth train go?' I shouted to the ticket clerk.

'They are all late today.'

'Ought we still to hurry?'

'Yes, yes, yes – be quick.'

This was hard. There were a great many steps, two children and two suitcases to be contended with. We had just landed safely on the other side, when the train arrived. Brenda held the door open and remained holding it until we were all safely inside.

'Bye bye, and thank you!'

'I'd do anything . . .' she said. 'Remember!'

The train pulled away. I fell back in the seat, my arms round each child. It didn't matter that my car was blocking the front of the post office or that I'd forgotten to pack myself any night things. We were on the right train, it was lunch time and there was fair weather ahead. I opened the bag of grapes. While we were all munching, I leant across to a middle-aged man who was sitting opposite and enquired amicably,

'What time does this train get into Portsmouth?'

'Portsmouth? This train isn't going to Portsmouth, it's the Littlehampton train.'

'What!'

I sprung to my feet, dropping the grapes into British Rail dust.

'It's twenty minutes late,' he said. 'All the trains were late today, the Portsmouth train is just behind.'

'This train seems to be running extra fast to make up for lost time.'

'Keep calm,' he said.

'I have a hospital appointment I can't miss. Can I take a taxi from Littlehampton?'

'You'd be better advised to change at Horsham and pick up the Portsmouth train.'

We stopped at Horsham and he helped us down.

'Now wait there on the platform,' he said. 'You mothers get so het up over things.'

It hadn't occurred to me that *he* might have been on the wrong train, until we had been standing for some minutes on an empty platform. Before the idea could take a hold, my eye caught the blank information board upon which the hand of an angel manufactured the word 'Portsmouth'. Almost immediately there was the sound of a train.

My mother was wearing red and looked very noticeable on the platform. She put Lili in a push chair, we loaded the cases and Doran onto a trolley, and headed for the ferry. Once she had kissed us all, I saw that not only was she wearing red, she was seeing red. Regardless of her boundless energy and youthful appearance, she had reached the age of sixty-five and had therefore been automatically retired. 'I'm spitting feathers,' she said.

'Darling mummy, I need you retired; you have a God given opportunity to help me.'

She understood, but I could see there were still a few feathers left to spit. When we were on the boat, and Lili and Doran were both competing for her knee, she began to forget she was angry.

My father was waiting anxiously on Ryde harbour.

'Daddy, isn't it lovely, we're all together?'

'I wish I wasn't driving you to hospital, Linda.'

'But it's exactly where I want to be.'

'I think you're very brave,' he said. 'This is beyond the call of duty.'

We all went up to the ward where I was presented with a bed. A weakness crept over me; I began to feel distinctly like an invalid. The sensation was lovely. They gave me a hospital nightdress and a pat on the head. I lay with my eyes softly closed. Time was suspended forever, or so I thought.

'Mrs Scotson?'

'Who?'

I was a white bird gliding in the sunshine.

The bird settled above the bed; I opened my eyes and located the heaviness of my human body and bright lights across the room. I didn't want to stay awake for long, so I tried not to develop the conversation.

'Mrs Scotson, I'm very sorry but we're having some trouble with your blood group.' This was sufficiently emotive to wake me up.

'We don't have any of it in stock.'

'Except in me; couldn't you take some out of me now, and put it back if you needed to?'

It seemed like a bright idea and I never found out why it wasn't taken seriously.

'Well, dear, wouldn't you rather go home for Christmas and come back on the twenty-seventh for your "op"? We'll have some blood over from Southampton by then.'

I began laughing; laughter picked me up, shook away my sleep and put me down again in the middle of my parents' living room. My father said, 'It's going to be a family Christmas after all.'

'As a special present,' I answered, 'could I teach you to pattern Doran *homolaterally*?'

We put a mattress on the kitchen table. With careful reference to the book, which travelled everywhere with me, the adults in the household learned how to move Doran's arms, legs and head in the first real crawling patterns of a baby. This took three people and lasted five minutes. Lili sat on a stool by her brother's head and sang Christmas carols to keep time and drown his intermittent protests.

'Could you do that four times a day while I'm away?'

They promised they would. Christmas was riotous. I slipped out unostentatiously on the twenty-seventh. Moe, Doran and Lili were on the floor under piles of toys.

I had taken considerable effort to avoid the rituals of shaving, injections of pethodine and the ubiquitous saline drip, when I went into labour. Now, in the course of my recovery, they were part of the package deal, and I was forced to welcome them. When the anaesthetic left me, I had no idea that I had slept through a whole day. I assessed my body cautiously to be sure the work was done. It was more thorough than I'd imagined. They had thrown in a catheter as an extra Christmas present.

I began to listen to my companions from other beds; great lines sprang from them. We shuttled homespun philosophy back and forth between each other.

I was given wildly conflicting opinions about my chances of being able to carry anything above a featherweight before the middle of March. By a stroke of genius, when my appointment at the Institutes arrived, it was for 25 March.

When Judy and Michael came to collect me, I discovered that there was an unusual amount of space in the outside world, and my legs felt disconcertingly weak. They put me to bed but I couldn't sleep.

'Judith, note that I sound very calm about this, but we have only two months to raise a thousand pounds.'

'Okay. If you can't sleep, write!'

We sent off a great many letters followed by instalments of my manuscript to *Woman's Own*.

Bert launched the second jumble sale which raised nearly eighty pounds, and left us with still more jumble. A group of businessmen from a charitable organization called 'the Lions' came to tea. Judith laid cups and saucers very prettily on a tray and tidied all the papers away under chairs. We anticipated a formal interview. When the men came in, they were full of boyish enthusiasm for our project. They would have drunk out of chipped mugs and not noticed. With very little preamble they said, 'We want to pay your air fare.'

This had the rare effect of reducing Judith to silence.

'I could hug you,' I said.

'DO,' they replied, putting down their tea cups.

As they left one of them turned to me, 'You are very lucky; you haven't got to worry about how to make your life worthwhile for the next few years.'

'You are very wonderful and very perceptive,' I said.

The next problem that was wiped away at a stroke was the fee for the first evaluation. Judith's father, Harris Levin, had

First morning at the Institutes, March 1980.

Lili, age 3, June 1980.

Crawling with the anti-roll device, May 1980, after 2 months on the programme.

Above left: After vertical pirouetting head up with Alison and Linda, November 1981.

Above: January 1981. First sitting in the 'god-awful', the forbidden position.

Left: November 1980 a first attempt at standing by Hillary's piano.

Above right: Creeping, Spring 1981, with anti-sit device and mask.

Right: Autumn 1981. Walking under ladders throughout the house.

Early morning start on the ladders, Summer 1981.

been gradually accumulating more data on the subject; he suddenly declared he would pay.

The winter drifted mildly away from the windows of Judith's house. One evening, when I was alone, a mischievous humour slipped under my skin and for no obvious reason I began to laugh.

Before Judith got back the phone went. It was my own father to tell me that my great aunt had died of a stroke a few hours before. Doran and Lili had both been in her room during her last moments of consciousness. He said she had seemed almost radiant and had asked for blue ribbons to be put in her hair.

When Judith came in I said, 'Birth is no gain, death is no loss.'

'What?'

'It's a quote from the Su Wen.'

'So?'

I explained. Judith said, 'I've had a quarter bottle of champagne in the fridge since Christmas. Let's toast Aunt Mabel.'

She opened it and we drank. I said, 'There is something faerie about the dear, dead lady. I think she'll be with us for a while.'

'I've decided you need to meet another woman, who's very much alive. She's your spiritual sister; her name is Magda.'

Magda had a degree in Anthropology and worked in a day-care centre for mentally handicapped adolescents; she came to supper. The conversation naturally turned on to the Institutes. Magda said, 'I understand what Glenn Doman's saying. I've visited some Institutions where children are simply changed, shuttled from beds to bean-bag chairs, and back to their beds again. In one home I met two young men who'd been out to work on a farm. I said, "That must be lovely for you." "No," they said. "We hate it." Linda, it was a chicken farm and they spent all day killing chickens.'

'Not to speak of it being cheap labour,' said Judith.

By the time the meal was over, Magda had set her mind on joining our journey to the Institutes.

'So,' I said, 'by now there is Doran, a poor brain injured, fatherless child, with his five women – Judith, Linda, Brenda, Magda and Lili – plus Aunt Mabel's ghost, on pilgrimage to Philadelphia.'

'Write and tell them he's Muslem and can't move a step without his harem,' said Magda.

The Institutes accepted our rapidly extending family with interest and humour. Magda's passage was looked after by an unexpected tax rebate which exactly covered her costs. Freddie Laker wrote to offer Brenda, Lili and I half fare, and a free flight for Doran. Judith was going back earlier to do some studying. She arranged to meet us at the airport and suggested we stay a few nights at her parents' home in Long Island.

Dianna came back briefly to buy one of my paintings, more money arrived from private donations. Judith felt secure enough to book us into a hotel in Chestnut Hill, ten minutes from the Institutes. A member of the Lions offered to take us to the airport. Magda was going to fly standby and meet us at the hotel.

By the beginning of March I was well enough to go over to the Isle of Wight and spend some time with my entire family before we flew out. I could see that if I provided another pair of hands we could pattern Doran eight times a day. My parents had already found two dedicated helpers. It seemed that everyone was impressed by the results.

Lili and my father met me off the boat. 'Doran's crawling,' she announced. 'She's not joking,' said my father. 'He can crawl three inches. You have two beautiful children.'

We came in through the back door; Doran was sitting on my mother's knee having tea. For a moment I saw his handicap from the point of view of a stranger. He was a handsome enough child, but his eyes were everywhere; his head lolled on his shoulders. His body, unlike his spirit, had little evidence of backbone.

'Doran!' I shouted affectionately, diving down to make love to his cheeks and ears. I could feel realization dawn upon him.

His mind struggled back, and the gap in time closed. Lili took my hand.

'Mummy, I want to show you my room, and bring Doran with you.'

The homecoming symbolized my physical restoration. The daffodils were out and the sun had a warm edge to it. We did eight patternings a day. Doran alternatingly rolled and crawled round the house. My father, more than anyone, spent his time on the floor with Doran.

'I love that little boy,' he would say. 'I want to take him fishing.'

Up till this point in our lives, I had no idea my father had any attachment to fishing.

Doran was less than good-humoured about his homolateral patterning. Once the five minutes were up, he indicated that he had shown great courage and forbearance, and demanded praise. He got a rousing chorus of 'For he's a Jolly Good Fellow' and was restored to the floor.

The day after we arrived home, a photographer from *Woman's Own* came. He positioned us in a thousand touching poses. I wanted Doran on his stomach, gritting his teeth and aiming for the next inch of carpet.

'That wouldn't do for a "TOA",' he said.

'A what?'

'A triumph over adversity story. It has to touch the heart.'

'But I wrote a lot of humour into that story. Have they edited it out?'

'You did write the funniest TOA I'd ever read . . . Would you mind kissing Doran on the cheek . . . just once more. Hold it.'

The next day, Southern Television came down and filmed an interview with me. Doran was extremely proud until he discovered that most of his time was going to be spent face downwards on the patterning table. He took a deep breath, turned crimson and roared continuously. It was not good for public relations. Fortunately, the camera team switched off the microphone.

The night before we left for New York, a somewhat sceptical friend resurrected a television set from his cellar and we went round to watch out for the story. During the patterning incident Doran appeared to be smiling. At the end of the interview, my friend scatched his head.

'What puzzles me,' he said, 'is that listening to you talk about that clinic on the box makes me almost believe you.'

8

---*---

THE PLANE TAXIED OUT along the runway and the engine grew louder. I was remembering swans wrench themselves free of water and spread their wings when the stewardess offered us tea.

'It'll make you feel better,' she said firmly.

While we sipped our drinks I reflected that after the initial climactic experience, we had to survive for seven hours in a restricted universe. Our altitude was now of less interest than the practical problem of finding space to pattern Doran. The front of the plane seemed plausible.

Lili undid her safety belt.

'Where are the other children?'

'We'll find them,' I said.

We made our way up towards the cockpit. Wherever I saw a family with children I paused to ask for help, until I had a platoon of volunteers. The stewardess laid down some blankets, the co-pilot stepped nonchalantly over Doran's head and all the juveniles on board trooped up to watch. Even more passengers found out about us when they queued for the toilets, so that Doran achieved sufficient fame to be given a standing ovation as he was carried out onto American soil. We were swept through the customs as if a brain injured child was too hot to handle, then Judith took him in her arms and directed us towards the taxi rank.

She explained that her father had been recalling some of the realities of the presence of children about the house and had therefore generously suggested paying for us at a hotel. She had chosen one in Manhattan, to give us two nights and a day to become New Yorkers before we were due in Philadelphia.

The cab driver had that familiar pessimism about the weather. 'Seems like there's a blizzard forecast. You'll be lucky to get out of New York by the weekend.'

'Ignore him,' Judith commanded. 'He's overreacting. Besides, it's too late in the year.'

The management showed us to our rooms, apologizing for the dirty carpets; the vacuum cleaner had broken down. We asked for extra sheets which we put over the floor. They made an unbroken landscape on which Doran and Lili rolled and crawled. Lili found some little round sweets in a dish by the radiator which I dissuaded her from eating and presented to the manager. He identified them as rat poison.

'You should have told me there were children,' he said.

'English hotels don't normally have rats.'

'This is America, lady.'

We discovered and removed several other similar dishes.

When Judith left for her parents' house on Long Island, Lili continued to sing and dance and make houses under the bed clothes. I thought Doran might sleep. Instead he developed raging pain in his gums. Brenda and I took turns to lie down with our eyes shut and our fingers in our ears. The alternative was to be passively danced over and blasted with song. The entertainment had the redeeming feature of distracting Doran from his unborn teeth.

When morning came a blizzard was outside. I found the bellboy and persuaded him to follow me back to our room. 'Would you mind turning a baby's head to left and right for five minutes, I'll explain why as we go.'

He was very obliging and acted as if he was used to more unusual requests.

Judith managed to get through the snow. 'Don't worry,' she said, 'it won't stick, at least not for long.'

Our eyelashes hung with snowflakes as we crunched along the sidewalks towards the Empire State Building.

The next night, I gave Doran a selection of different remedies I'd collected for toothache. The effect was negligible.

In the morning Michael arrived with Judith, and a car which he'd hired to drive us to Philadelphia. The snow melted as we travelled south along straight highways until our way was signposted to Chestnut Hill, a small village on the outskirts of the city. The Chestnut Hill Hotel gave cheap rates for Institutes families. We were therefore unprepared for the elegance of the building, with its portico supported by pillars, and ladies and gentlemen in evening dress gliding in and out through the doors.

We staggered in past a very expensive looking restaurant and on up to reception.

'This must be the wrong place,' said Brenda. 'They can't want brain injured children here.'

We stared at the carpet, imagining it littered with writhing bodies trying to crawl. In reality we saw a pair of bare brown feet with painted toe nails. Our eyes travelled up from the hem of a sari, towards the caste mark on the forehead of our manageress.

'Good evening, I'm Sheila. Let me show you to your rooms.'

Michael left to drive back to Vermont. He would collect us at the end of the week.

Our accommodation was spacious and included a bathroom. Before we had finished unpacking, Magda arrived. We were, as planned, close to the Institutes and together.

That night Lili, Doran, Brenda and I lay in the same bed. Lili slept, but Doran continued to suffer indescribably with his teeth. By five a.m. it seemed worth taking him out on to the landing. I had a toy I'd bought in New York, which was too noisy for the bedroom so I picked it up and groped my way out. The landing light was dim. A young man lay drowsing on the sofa in front of the TV. He stirred and sat up.

'You'd like some coffee?'

'Who are you?'

'I help out here nights. Coffee?'

'Please.'

He continued to fill up my cup. Doran was prepared to be distracted from his suffering.

'You wait till the rest get up,' said my new friend.

'Who are they?'

'The other Institutes families booked in here; this place is kept running by the Institutes.'

'What about the restaurant?'

'That's not owned by the hotel. It's pretty classy.'

By six-thirty the first coughs and cries could be heard. The door opposite opened and I heard a strong Liverpudlian voice calling, 'Come on, our Susan. How many bloody times do I have to bloody tell you?'

Next door a woman shouted, 'André, André, come here this minute.'

A small earthquake seemed to be shaking the Chestnut Hill Hotel.

The landing was arranged with chairs, tables and a sideboard on which Sheila put out cake and cereal for breakfast. While I was feeding Doran his conventional egg, a large square man with a grey pointed beard in the mould of Ernest Hemingway cut himself some cake and sat down. His wife and son followed him to the table. The boy looked about fourteen and was so bright and animated that I couldn't believe he was brain injured. His mother told me they were Canadian and had come because their son had a reading problem, but she was also wondering if the clinic could do something about his hearing. He was stone deaf.

All of us seemed to have first appointments about the same time, 8.30 a.m., and we gathered outside for taxis. Our cab finally turned into Stenton Avenue and we saw a high stone wall with a sign 'The Institutes for the Achievement of Human Potential' jutting out from it. We turned through the gateway past another sign which read – 'Drive slowly. Children every-where' – and pulled up before the door of a very European looking manor house. The staff were waiting in the hallway to welcome us. Their enthusiasm presupposed that they appreci-ated we'd come through fire and water to get to them. We had our names pinned to us and sat together in what appeared to be a long, late Victorian dining-room hung with portraits.

Instantly we were chaperoned by a tall red-haired girl who told us whom we would meet that day, and what the procedures were.

The other twenty-seven families sat holding their children in their arms, or by the hands, depending upon their degree of mobility or hyperactivity, while the staff talked gently to them. It was evident how much consideration had been taken to reassure us and make us feel at home. The atmosphere was more like the first term at university than an introduction to a clinic for sick children.

I felt heady and euphoric.

'Welcome to the Institutes, Mrs Scotson. How do you feel? You've had quite a journey.'

'Great, absolutely great!'

'Is this Dor-ran?'

'Hi, Dor-ran, and Lili? Where's Lili?'

Lili emerged from her expeditions into international conversation and began to correct the Americans on their English.

The work of assessing the children developed in an orderly fashion. We learned that the Institutes divided itself into the Institutes for Physical, Physiological and Intellectual Excellence. Today the children were to be assessed in each to determine whether or not they were in fact brain injured. Doran's assessment proved positive. I was in no real doubt of this but it was good to have crossed the last barrier to beginning the full treatment programme. I hugged Doran and remarked, 'As Churchill said, "This is not the end. It is not even the beginning of the end. But it is, perhaps, the end of the beginning".'

We went into Bruce Hagy's office to be told formally the results of the first day's evaluation. He held out his hand, 'Congratulations, your child is brain injured. We can help you.'

'Nowhere else on earth could I expect to be congratulated on Doran's condition. But then where else could I expect to be helped?'

'Right,' he said smiling.

Doran had a diffuse mid-brain injury; details of which would become clear in the next few days.

We had another early appointment. The clinic was within the grounds of the old house and rose with simple grace from the sloping woodland. There was a single large carpeted room with a high ceiling, round which were short flights of stairs leading to open-sided corridors and evaluation rooms. Downstairs there were more offices and equipment.

Part of the main room had a barrier round it. Here the floor surface differed; there was thick pile carpet, hardboard and Plexiglass. Each presented a different answer to problems of mobility. Some of the smaller children with little or no movement had already found their way there. I stretched out on the thick pile beside Doran and closed my eyes. Lili was still occupied giving English lessons. There were chairs round the walls and a few high tables with padded vinyl surfaces. At first the families sat shyly and diffidently on the chairs. Then one by one they put their children on the floor and lay beside them, suggesting they crawl. Judith shook me.

'Doran's rolling over to that little Downs Syndrome girl. Do you want to see him flirt? She has the most engaging eyes.'

I struggled back into consciousness.

The staff managed to be everywhere and families were regularly swept into one or other of the evaluation rooms. A calm order reigned over what could have been chaos.

We decided to pattern Doran at one of the tables and began at a good pace, singing 'Green Grow the Rushes O'.

A dark-haired young woman with an English rose complexion came towards us. She waited politely until we'd finished and then spoke.

'It's good to see you trying out our tables.' She held out her hand. 'Mrs Scotson, good morning, I'm your advocate. My name is Rosalind Klein. Did you get some sleep?'

'I'm not sure but I feel wonderful.'

She raised her eyebrows and continued, 'All the Institutes staff have close contact with our families but we like to ensure that each child has a very special person immediately available and responsible for him. That's why we have the advocate system. So while you're at the Institutes I shall be looking after Doran.'

'You're lovely. I'm delighted.'

'Thank you. Now would you like to come to my office so that I can take a closer look at that young man?'

Rosalind was also the Associate Director of the Institute for the Achievement of Physical Growth. We sat in a semi-circle while Doran demonstrated his crawling and great deal of rolling. Rosalind shook her head, 'Doran, you're about the best roller I've ever seen.'

'Was that a compliment or a criticism?' I asked.

'Both. His rolling is really superb but it doesn't lead anywhere except to more rolling. Kids who roll well don't bother to crawl. Crawling is vital for Doran's neurological reorganization. How far can he crawl?'

'Three inches.'

'He needs to crawl a thousand feet in a day to turn into a creeper. Creeping's one major achievement for a mid-brain.'

'A creeper?' I envisaged some kind of climbing plant.

'Mrs Scotson, I mean to get Doran up off the ground crawling on his hands and knees.'

'Ah, not a parasitic vegetable?'

Rosalind laughed. She was collecting the necessary information to determine Doran's neurological age. We were not hurried or pushed, there was no fear that anything would be misunderstood. She had just discovered Doran hadn't lost the infantile babinski reflex in his feet (causing the toes to extend as you scratch the sole of the foot). When I noticed her take off one of her shoes I supposed it was simply the sort of thing Americans did in relaxed moments. The next minute she was beating it loudly under the table. We all jumped violently except Doran, who looked a little amused. Rosalind repeated the sound and we reproduced our responses.

'What happened to you, Doran? Well done the rest of you; you have pretty good startle reflexes.'

'Do you like doing that?' asked Judith.

'Making people jump out of their skins? It's all part of the job here. Now if you would all follow me downstairs, I have another surprise waiting.'

We walked after her into a strange room which had a low rectangular box on the floor. She turned off the light and pressed a button on the side of the box. We were blasted by a sound like an air raid siren, accompanied by a blinding flash of light. We didn't merely jump, we screamed, all except for Doran who remained silent. When Rosalind put the light back on he looked positively disappointed.

'You four have a highly developed vital response to threatening sounds,' she said. 'Doran's needs a little help.'

'I think he liked it,' said Magda.

'I'll never recover,' I said.

'We usually start treating the parents pretty soon after we've fixed up the children.'

We went back to the office and continued with the evaluation. When it was over Judith suggested coffee.

'Do you realize,' I said, 'that that was already the most thorough examination Doran has ever had in his life – and we've only just started?'

'Do you remember everything we got through?' Judith asked.

Magda had made notes.

'Visual, auditory, tactile and manual competence, babinski, startle reflex, vital response to threatening sounds and language. All the problems are related to his mid-brain injury.'

Despite the considerable emphasis on healthy eating habits and vitamin pills, coffee seemed vital for everyone's survival. I noticed how much more the families wanted to nod and smile at each other to indicate they were sharing something of the same experience. We watched an Australian couple spending their time goodnaturedly intercepting their hyperactive son. The child was about ten years old and moved like greased lightning. I never found out how they held him down for the flight over; they didn't have time for conversation.

Nobody minded waiting for appointments because it was

clear that each family would have all the attention they needed when their time came. While Lili lay on the floor talking to children, and making no distinction between who was brain injured and who was not, Doran had an appointment with Dr 'Bob' Doman.

'Respect for parents seems to come naturally here,' I said.

'We learn so much from you people, and you're the ones who go home and do the job with your kids, not us.'

He worked his way down Doran's back. It was perfect. Doran had been saved from the enforced seated posture which might have curved his spine, or deformed his hip joints.

Soon Dr Doman had his own file of statistics. Doran grinned unevenly.

'That,' he said, 'is a mid-brain smile. You know mid-brains are so damn charming. I remember fixing up a kid with a smile like that. The boy's a doctor now, but he still has the same slightly crooked smile.'

The last evaluation before lunch was to check Doran's respiration. I was surprised to discover how shallow and irregular it was. The vital factor was that it could be changed and that improved breathing would bring better coordination.

We were hungry. From my point of view the food was perfect; bowls and bowls of salad, fruit, yogurt and cottage cheese. The sight of so much salad sent non-vegetarians into an initial panic. It was not, however, obligatory to have a bowl of raw cauliflower; plenty of meat and cooked vegetables were available. Most families had difficulty in feeding their children. Giving a brain injured child a small meal can take half a day. Since no one had that long to spare, squashed banana and milk was a general favourite.

Besides the staff and parents, we were also catching sight of groups of young men and women who appeared either in tracksuits or rather smart blazers, white shirts, and black trousers or skirts. Magda had discovered that they were students at the School for Human Development, which was yet another part of the Institutes.

'They come here after doing two years on a home programme,' she said. 'They were telling me what their routine is like. They do miles and miles of crawling and creeping.'

'That's what you and Doran will be doing, Linda. Better get your knee-pads on,' Judith exclaimed cheerfully.

We went back to the clinic. The air was clear and cold. Some of the parents were standing outside smoking. A girl of about eleven or twelve took my hand and asked who I wanted to see. 'I'll take you,' she said, and then looking at Doran, 'How old is he? What's his name?'

'He's eighteen months and his name is Doran.'

'Is he brain injured?'

'Yes.'

'What's his name?'

'Doran.'

We repeated our conversation until the woman from Liverpool came up and asked me if I'd seen the doctor.

'Not recently.'

'It's Susan, she's having a fit,' she said calmly, walking away before I could answer. When it was time to have Doran's measurements taken the details were recorded at length: height, weight, chest, head, pelvis, even the degree of flesh on his bones. Doran strongly objected to being reduced to a list, but when he was sure it was over he took a deep breath, returned to his normal colour and smiled.

'That means it was nothing personal,' I said.

'I'm glad to hear that, Doran.' Elaine Lee shook his hand. 'Ludwina wants you now for Intelligence.'

We were directed next door. Doran looked pleased by the absence of measuring instruments. Lili took the initiative.

'Doran can read,' she said.

'That's wonderful, Lili. Did you teach him?'

Lili nodded. 'But he can't speak.'

'Can he take a card?'

'No,' I said, 'but he could point to it.'

She handed me a large red felt tipped pen and some white cards.

'Write some of his favourite words.'

I made a selection. Ludwina held up 'Mummy' and 'Doran'.

'Doran, which card is "Mummy"?'

Slowly, his hand went up and touched the right card. She tried three times and each time Doran triumphed.

'Good man,' she said. 'Do you want to show me your reading, Lili?' The interview progressed. Ludwina showed Doran some new words and tested him on them immediately. He had no trouble with identification; his manner was confident and charming.

'Doran expects to be taken seriously,' I said. 'I find it almost shocking.'

'We can shock you?' Ludwina enquired.

'Apparently, in the course of dealing with brain injury. If a doctor listens to a mother it's usually to make her feel better, not to learn something that will help her child.'

'That's because he doesn't believe there is a way,' said Magda.

'That's true,' I said.

'This is so different, I have to be careful to be precise about Doran, because I know the staff are really listening.'

By the time we were back at the hotel it was past eight o'clock. We were supposed to get a good night's sleep. A three month course in neurological reorganization and human development had to be crammed into the next two days. To keep us awake and intellectually receptive, we were asked to wear warm clothes, and to expect air conditioning rather than central heating. This seemed to worry the Floridians but could hardly affect the English. A new kind of camaraderie began to flourish at the Chestnut Hill Hotel. The Liverpudlians were fraternizing with Trinidad and Canada and large piles of beer cans proclaimed the extent of familiarity. Although tempted by the conversation and laughter, my good sense suggested that I put Lili in the bath and climb in after her with Doran in my arms. I had forgotten that children don't keep still in water and I had no idea how different the American system of plugs and showers could be. The bath was drained several times while hot and cold deluges rained upon us. When they were finally picturesque and exhausted they lay on either side of me in the bed. I could hear the man from Liverpool quite clearly outside my door. He was describing the long search to find help for his daughter, Susan. Francis's great love for his child combined with an hilarious anecdotal humour, the most favoured word of which was 'bloody'. I was lulled to sleep with the story of the Natureopath who recommended coffee enemas.

'So I went to the best bloody coffee shop in Liverpool and asked for half a pound of coffee. He says to me, "Do you want Mocha or Brazilian?" So I said, "Where that's going no one will taste the bloody difference!"'

Judith took the prospect of the cold lecture theatre seriously and exhorted us all to borrow rugs and blankets from the hotel, as well as wearing coats, gloves and two pairs of socks.

'You'll thank me for this when the time comes,' she muttered from behind a pile of borrowed bedding.

We knew that even if we were about to disagree with every word Glenn Doman said, we owed him thanks for respecting us and uniquely representing the argument against the classical treatment of our children. We were by now under no misapprehension about the extent of the problem and the work involved; and if we had been, the next two days would have quickly dispelled our illusions.

Glenn was aware he was speaking to a group of parents rather than a group of doctors. He reached us through our experience. We understood him because he had a keen insight into us.

He stressed that the brain runs everything and that since brain injury is in the brain, the failure to cure it has been by persistently treating the symptoms instead of the cause. The dead cells were dead and gone, the aim was to reorganize the living cells to take over their function. When he suggested that brain injured children were not sick – they were hurt – we could instantly make the philosophical distinction. We didn't live in a world of precise medical terminology but we had all spent months or years resolutely assessing our children.

He used a simple analogy: 'The brain, like the biceps, grows through use.' If all the sensory pathways to the brain are stimulated, the brain grows.

There were five main factors. The children had to be provided with normal developmental opportunities, which was impossible if they were strapped up in calipers and special chairs. They had to have the normal pattern of development imposed on them, and their neurological organization enhanced. It was important to establish the dominance of right or left, and, most essential, it was vital to enhance their ability to breathe.

After fifty minutes a bell rang indicating that we could rush out and refresh ourselves. We had all been armed with large folders and paper, and had feverishly taken notes. Each of us could already identify our own child from the content of the lecture.

'I never thought I'd hear someone say that mothers know more about their children than doctors,' said Magda.

'We're all to blame for turning our doctors into gods,' I said. 'The question is, can we help them down amongst the common people?'

'The trouble with Linda is she's too emotionally involved with Doran, for us to take her ideas seriously,' said Judith. 'Don't hit me, I was only joking.'

The bell went and we dashed back to our seats. It was only by the second coffee break that I remembered we'd been warned about the cold. After lunch the lectures were equally compelling but by this time I'd acepted one of Judith's rugs.

During supper we compared notes. Magda opened her folder.

'Just looking through, what strikes me is the simple way the staff express themselves.'

'They don't have to confuse you to hide their ignorance,' Brenda said. 'They know what they're talking about.'

Magda read, '"Brain injury creates a barrier between the environment and the brain. The more severe the injury, the thicker the barrier. As a general rule, the more functions the barrier intercepts, the more general the injury."'

Judith pointed further down the page, 'This is a good description of what the Institutes do. Linda will be asked that question over and over again.'

'Judith,' I said, 'I can tell you now; they give children visual, auditory and tactile stimulation with increased frequency, intensity and duration in recognition of the orderly way in which the brain grows. Applause please.'

I was aware that although people would help me out of sheer goodness, most would also want to know why they were doing it. The families had been frequently told that there was no guarantee that each individual child would get well. The Institutes still did not know enough, but they were continually researching. We were encouraged to question, think and connect.

It was ten o'clock before we trooped back to the clinic to retrieve our children. Even the most hyperactive seemed reasonably drowsy.

Lili ran up to me, 'Mummy, Doran's hungry. I've been giving him orange juice.'

Doran was on the knee of a staff member sucking his bottle.

'Mrs Scotson, your son has the most incredible appetite. Where does he put it?'

'Into his nappy, and in vast amounts,' Judith cut in. We took the bottle with Doran still attached to it, thanked everyone we could, and ordered a taxi back to the hotel. Beer cans had emerged again and a castle of them was rising gradually from the table. Francis was explaining how he once got a peanut lodged in his sinuses.

Next morning in the lecture theatre Gretchen Kerr explained the Institutes' developing profile. This was a graphic tool for plotting a child's neurological age against chronological age. It allowed you to see the degree of injury your child had, and the path his recovery would take. It was the sequence of human development written down. I began to see how Doran's function compared with normal growth, and the kind of achievements he would have to make to catch up. When Douglas

Doman, Glenn's son, lectured on the floor programme it became very clear that crawling was vital for intellectual and physical growth, which was dependent upon neurological organization.

Friday arrived and we waited in the Clinic with a list of appointments. Doran's daily life was about to be given extremely precise structure. We arrived in Rosalind's office to digest the Initial Floor Programme. She handed us sheets of instructions which she proceeded to augment.

'Doran must be on the floor day and night, and all visitors must obey the rules of the floor. Every moment Doran spends on the floor in the prone position, he has the opportunity for movement. That is giving him the best environment to become well. The only exception to him being on the floor are for reward, companionship, food, and to go to the bathroom.'

'I already live on the floor,' I said. 'It's more natural to me than chairs.'

'Good. Now the most important law for Doran is that he must never roll.'

'How do I stop him?'

'Since the man is such an expert, he needs to wear an anti-roll device.'

She produced a large aluminium cross fitted to a canvas waistcoat. It was to be worn in such a way that if its occupant attempted to roll, its spokes would hit the ground first and prevent him. Doran admired the invention. I said, 'Once he puts his energy into crawling he'll be magnificent.'

'Good, because we have a tough goal for him. He needs to be able to crawl a thousand feet in a day.'

Judith said, 'Where does she find a thousand feet in her tiny cottage?'

'He goes round in circles,' I replied.

'Good,' said Rosalind, 'provided he doesn't get giddy and crash into the table. All the time he spends on the floor in the prone position, he's having the optimum chance to get well, so Doran will sleep on the floor on his stomach.'

'I understand, and with his head away from the wall so that he can crawl in his sleep.'

'What about rolling?' asked Judith.

'No problem,' Rosalind answered. 'Doran will sleep in his anti-roll device.'

Doran usually slept in the crook of my arm. 'That'll make a change for him,' I said, 'but it doesn't worry me.'

Judith was incredulous. 'Brenda will have to drag you apart and put a sword between you.'

'Look,' I said, 'we needed a whole new way of life, now we've got one, and I'm delighted.'

I could see that Rosalind believed me. She met my eyes. 'Any questions?'

'None on that score.'

We went over the daily life of the Floor Programme. At last Rosalind said, 'The only thing I have left to tell you, you already know. Enjoy it! Doran's attitude will reflect your own.'

'She'll have a riot,' said Judith.

Rosalind raised her eyebrows and held out her hand.

We had got into the habit of patterning Doran between his appointments. When the time came for us to be officially taught, our style was improved. We learned to push out Doran's fingers and slide his opened palms along the table. The importance of tactile information was stressed, and the number of patternings increased from eight to fifteen.

When we got outside Judith said, 'You're going to have a lot of organizing to do. It won't come naturally to you.'

'Look, this programme is a structure. It makes order out of chaos. Once I've learnt how to do it, life is actually going to be easier.'

'But structure has hardly been part of your life,' said Judith.

'It's been my entire life. Maybe you don't understand painting. Every little part of it is dependent on every other little part, but when you look at the whole thing, you don't think of that!'

Judith pointed out that we had Nutrition next on our schedule, and if we didn't want to be hungry while we were getting it, perhaps we ought to have lunch.

Nutrition was no shock to me. We didn't eat sugar or refined foods and I was already fascinated by vitamins. I could easily replace salt with garlic and kelp powder and hope friends would enjoy their health-giving properties and forgive the pungent fumes and vivid evocations of rotting seaweed. The blue folder I had been given before the lecture increased in weight and volume. The families around us must have been overtired and under stress but they all looked positively cheerful.

We had quite a long wait between the next three appointments. Masking, Intelligence and the Overview. Masking was a method of improving the depth of a child's respiration and to increase the level of oxygen in the blood. It also patterned the brain with clear information about deep breathing. In a stuffy atmosphere where there is a higher level of carbon dioxide, even brain injured children automatically breathe more deeply to adjust the balance. Carbon dioxide dilates the blood vessels which helps the flow of oxygen to the brain. Doran was to wear a small plastic mask with a tube at the bottom admitting a little air over his nose and mouth for periods of one minute, sixty times a day. The rules for using this were naturally very serious. Nevertheless, the reality of getting sixty one minute maskings into a day had hilarious overtones. I would need an egg timer continuously set for seven minute intervals. I could see myself falling over chairs, toys and children to get to Doran each time the bell rang. We were given a huge pile of masks and a pat on the back.

The Intelligence programme was a much more comprehensive development of Doran's reading. I wrote down the quantities; fifty reading words each day, divided into ten categories of five words in each, to be taught once or twice a day, in ten or twenty, five minute sessions.

Magda said, 'When I get back from America I'll do the words and bring them down to you every weekend.'

Doran eyed the stack of bright demonstration cards covetously. Ludwina handed him one as a present. The large red letters proclaimed the word 'Astronaut'.

'He's real smart,' she said. 'The Intelligence programme creates the need to move. It will be his best friend. Now, is there anything you don't understand?'

There wasn't. Everything we had been taught fitted into a closely knit pattern and I was consumed with an eagerness to develop it.

We had eaten a late supper and drunk many cups of coffee before the Overview. Lili and Doran sensed the impending end of the excitement. They both unexpectedly relaxed into sleep.

When the time came to talk to Bruce Haigey, to ensure he had an encompassing perspective of our commitment, a strong feeling of intoxication crept over me again. I knew these were my last moments of independence before the real work began.

Brenda and Judith carried my dreaming children into the office and we sat together in a line waiting for the interview to begin. Bruce had scarcely shaken our hands when the phone rang. Despite the lateness of the evening the clinic was still energetically functioning. He apologized and headed off to another case. He had just arrived back and extended his hand when someone called him from the door. By the third time he returned. His words had grown more distant. My eyelids became hypnotically heavy. When I tried to open them I could see two images of Bruce. Judith began to shake me.

'I'm sorry,' I yawned, 'I seem to be asleep.'

He suggested coffee and cool air and with some effort I left for the dining room. As I crossed the garden and mounted the steps to the old building, other parents were packing up ready to leave.

'See you in June. Good luck.'

I tried to imagine the grounds in summer. As I drank, the image of Doran crawling one thousand feet, even ten feet, roused me completely. I ran back to the evaluation room.

Bruce didn't seem the least perturbed. I discovered he wanted me awake to congratulate me for standing up to the week's work. It was a parting ceremony I'd not expected.

'Here you are, being lovely, and I crumple up in front of you and sleep.'

'My advice is to go home and rest up for a week.'

'I would, if I could induce Doran to see the sense in it.'

Doran looked completely peaceful. It was hard to believe the extent of his usual restless energy.

'We want you to relax and get back to normal before you make your decision whether or not to put Doran on our programme.'

'I know why you want me to wait, and I appreciate that, but I am already sure. There is no doubt in my mind.'

'She's right,' said Judith. 'She'll do it.'

Bruce must have realized there was commitment behind the euphoria. He didn't repeat himself.

'We'll see you in June,' I said.

He stood up and shook hands.

'We look forward to meeting you again. Doran should be doing some great crawling by then.'

'A thousand feet,' I said, 'with ease.'

9

JUDITH AND MICHAEL took us to Kennedy Airport and wished us bon voyage! Magda had already gone north to visit some relations.

Both children fell asleep soon after take off. Brenda announced her intention of staying awake until she'd had supper. I could neither eat nor sleep. Doran's situation was urgent, and the three months to the next appointment would go quickly; I had a superb script but we needed a cast of thousands for the performance. I wondered how many patterners Bert had found in England. Every time I closed my eyes I wanted to get up and do something. Lili was curled in the seat beside me while Doran lay at my feet cocooned in blankets. He was still sucking his dummy and snoring as we flew into Sunday morning and touched down. Bert met us at the airport; she had a reporter and a photographer in tow.

'You need people, luv, and you've got to keep them in touch, so you must have your press.'

Since Doran was still asleep in my arms and in no position to give an interview, I said, 'I've had one of the most positive experiences of my life, but we have hard work ahead and we need help.'

On the way home Bert told me that volunteers were slow coming forward.

'How many?'

'Look, I'm not talking about your close friends because they'd all lend a hand, but most of us have to work, or live a long way off.'

'I know, so how many?'

'So far we've had one telephone call.'

'One!'

'From a woman called Judy Blowe; she helped in our last jumble sale. She's very good at organizing and she's heard of the Institutes. We've booked the Parish Hall so that you can give a talk and demonstration patterning with Doran. Hopefully people will come.'

'When for?'

'Next week. I decided you'd need time to recover.'

'I do and I don't. I have to get started; I'll be ill if I wait.'

Somehow we struggled through the unpacking, then I phoned up everyone I could think of about patterning. Most people were willing to come once or twice but couldn't commit themselves beyond that. Finally I phoned up two friends, Sue Bittleston and Jaya Graves. They lived in a large house which had been divided into flats and let to young people who were students at the Rudolf Steiner College in Forest Row, or who had children at the Steiner school.

Sue and Jaya agreed to coordinate groups for each day. In the meantime they promised that the residents of the house would fill in between going to their lectures and picking up and delivering their children. The outlook was rosier, but when Bert had gone and the children were in bed, I sensed an unease in Brenda.

'It's no good,' she said. 'I need some other job that gives me independence. I think what you're doing for Doran is wonderful but I can't stay and do it all the time. I know it wouldn't work.'

'But I need you.'

'You won't once you've found all these people to come in and help. I shan't leave the district but I must have my own work.'

I understood her feelings because I knew how important it was to have something of one's own. Now I had a new situation; I needed to be strong enough to be very dependent upon both friends and strangers.

Next morning, with a keen sense of my own responsibility,

I got up early and, leaving the children still dreaming and jet lagged, I began to look for the spare bits of lino I remembered being left over from the bathroom floor. Doran was supposed to crawl his thousand feet on a smooth surface, which would make it easier. I pushed the sofa to the other side of the room. The noise woke Brenda who came down.

'Good heavens, whatever are you doing? Can't we all have the chance to sleep.'

'I have to get started.'

'Didn't the Institutes say wait?'

'Yes, but they didn't intend to send me mad first; I have all this energy. I'll rest when Doran's well.'

There was a cry upstairs. Lili called out, 'Mummy, Doran's awake.'

Brenda took my hand, 'You go to them, Linda, I'll finish this.'

By the time breakfast was over she had laid lino and measured the house. She wrote the lengths of each room in big red figures and stuck them on the wall.

'I'll work with you in the mornings,' she said, 'but after lunch I'll go out and look for a job.'

We took it in turns to stop Doran rolling, and discovered that the most efficient way of masking was to pin him to the floor on his stomach so that he couldn't struggle. I used the timer on the stove. If it was an imposition on Doran to have every eighth minute of his life occupied with a plastic bag over his nose, it was an ever greater imposition on me. Every time I was about to get up and do something, the buzzer pulled me back to the mask.

I had my hopes set on the meeting in the Parish Hall. The newspapers carried stories on the subject, it wasn't unreasonable to expect a crowd. In fact the hall was nearly empty. Judy and Bert were there with a small group from the Lions, and one or two people I didn't know.

Since Doran was well wrapped up I put him down on the cold linoleum and talked about his floor programme. Then Brenda, Bert and I patterned him, on an uncomfortably low table. A woman in the front row asked if he found the exercises strenuous.

'Wouldn't a normal two-year-old be wrecking the house by now? Doran can't do enough to tire himself out; that's one reason why he doesn't sleep.'

To my surprise she nodded, 'You're right. I mean he's not moving at all, and I find it difficult to keep my son still.'

After I'd finished, the same young woman, who had a very pretty, earnest face with a knitted hat pulled firmly down all round it, came up to me.

'My name is Kirsteen Whitby,' she said. 'I admire what you're doing and I'll help. What's more, I'll find as many people as possible to bring along to see if they want to join in.'

The group from the Lions were chatting to Bert and Judy. Bert was enthusiastic.

'They're from Uckfield, Linda, and they'd like to send a team down on Thursday evenings.'

The situation looked so hopeful that I was inspired to take some more initiative and try the church magazine. The editor was forthright.

'I'm going to find you all the "doers" in the Parish. The people with time on their hands are always too busy to help. When do you want to begin?'

'On Monday.'

Brenda found a gardening job and decided to spend part of the week sharing a flat with a friend, closer to where she would work. By now I had a temporary plan of the week's teams and I trusted that Sue and Jaya would send friends to fill in the spaces.

On Sunday night Brenda tidied and swept the house for me. In the morning a pile of reading cards arrived from Magda with a note saying she would be down the following weekend. By the time Brenda left for work Doran was on the floor watching Lili, who was stacking bricks for him, and being regularly masked.

I knew that from this date until we were back at the Institutes he was going to have fifteen patternings a day.

At ten o'clock, two women from the church choir arrived. They were kind and receptive. The whole morning passed in an orderly way with Lili explaining anything she thought I might have missed and Doran allowing his limbs to be imposed on until we'd found the right rhythm. I had no idea who my friends would send in the afternoon.

It was Kirsteen. She'd found a lift and brought four other people with her. The guests had children. I could hear books and toys tumble off the shelves round us as we worked. In the middle of some robust singing and manipulating a photographer appeared unannounced, surprisingly unaware of who or what he was supposed to be photographing. He pulled a crumpled piece of paper from his pocket in the hope of getting some insight.

'You can do what you like,' I said, 'but don't stop the flow.'

I put Doran on to the lino, masked him and urged him forward. The chaos plainly motivated him; he thrashed his way towards it at every opportunity.

Kirsteen said, 'He's lovely. People are daft, Linda; when I asked one lady to come she said, "If only his mother didn't call the little boy 'brain injured' she'd get more help."'

'If being brain injured doesn't make you worth assistance I'd like to know what does.'

'She was scared of what Doran would look like. She thought his brains would be running out of his ears.'

Since I needed all the time these friends could give, I didn't make rules about putting toys away. I tidied between maskings with the frenetic speed of a two-year-old.

The kitchen table, although ideal for size, was proving to be a little low if you had to bend over it fifteen times a day; a plea went out for some blocks of wood to prop it up. Between explanations I was showing the reading cards without muddling them, doing the maskings, giving Doran doses of vitamins to dry up his catarrh and making cups of tea.

I refused to accept even mildly negative remarks. When asked, 'Doesn't it take up a lot of time?' I replied, 'If it didn't, I'd want to know why not!'

In the evening Diana Phillips who owned the whole-food shop in the village arrived with a friend. 'It's about time the village had a good cause,' she said. 'This should shake them up a bit.'

She was a strong, intelligent woman in her late fifties. Some people were a little afraid of her because she spoke her mind so honestly. Doran loved her. After the fifteenth session we shook hands. 'We made it,' I said. 'The first day is over.'

'May you have many more,' said Diana.

I continued the floor programme until about ten o'clock when Doran seemed reasonably tired. Then I settled him on his mattress on the floor by the bed, put his dummy in his mouth and wished him good night and good crawling. Lili was already asleep on my pillow. She had enjoyed the day; visitors were magic to her and there was to be no shortage of them.

Every morning at ten o'clock two or three energetic people with, or without a group of children around them, appeared and set to work. Doran submitted to many untutored hands; whatever his superficial thoughts on the daily routine, the atmosphere was good-humoured even comic. We pressed on singing through his protests, until one of my new friends said, 'Actually he's not complaining, he's joining in. Listen.'

The sound coming from Doran had the distinct rhythm of 'Ten Green Bottles'.

After five days Doran was moving significantly further and, since he crawled with bare knees, elbows and feet to provide maximum tactile information, he was also considerably dirtier. It wasn't enough to vacuum my floor every night; it would have to be washed. I swamped it with strong detergents.

Magda came on Saturday bearing an aluminium anti-roll device, which she fitted to a smart maroon jacket. Doran could just squeeze through the kitchen door wearing it. The shape was plausibly the scaffolding for a turtle shell without the body work. Once it was on Doran didn't roll but instead of being disappointed and sulking, he simply put more effort into moving forward.

'Let's advertise our policies,' Magda said. She wrote out

some large notices in felt-tip and stuck them on the walls. She began with the command 'Be joyous!' – and 'The key to the motor pathways is opportunity' – and of course, 'Time is the enemy of the brain injured child'.

Then she sat down and stencilled out another pack of word cards. My new way of life seemed the most eccentric I'd yet chosen. An old friend, and teacher at the local school, who came on Saturday afternoon, felt I was living in an ivory tower, 'Linda, do you ever read the newspaper or listen to the radio?'

'No.'

'But the news is dreadful. What would you do if there was a war?'

'I haven't time to worry about that.'

'But don't you think you should?'

'I believe every positive act pulls us back from the brink. Getting Doran well is what I have to offer.'

'Nevertheless I think I should keep a log of current affairs and read them to you while we work.'

Magda stayed the night. After the experience of two staggered meal times in which I fed everyone separately, breaking off every seven minutes to obey the bell and attend to Doran, she offered to cook a nut roast for lunch.

'How will you do it?'

'In the robot chef; it'll be very quick.'

She looked at the pristine machine on top of my refrigerator. I'd bought it with a gift from the Artists Benevolent Fund in order to make cooking in these conditions swift and painless.

'Haven't you used it yet?' she said suspiciously.

'I lost the instructions.'

'Linda!'

'Well the blade looks sharp,' I answered sheepishly, 'and the plastic bowl came off, I can't fix it on properly. It's awfully difficult to think about new things between maskings.'

Magda laughed and said, 'Watch, the process is unbelievably simple.' We ate on the floor but we ate simultaneously. Doran's digestion continued to be unaffected by his position.

In the afternoon Kirsteen and her entire family came over with Diana. Gradually, seven minute conversations became possible. I asked Kirsteen why she'd come to my talk.

'I was curious about you, I'd heard a lot of rumours about Doran's birth. I want my next child born at home. I heard the doctors here had decided to stop home deliveries and it was put down to the fuss you were making about Doran.'

'I couldn't grieve and forget; Doran wasn't dead. I wanted something done.'

'At that time I was so angry that I could have strangled you with a silk scarf.'

'A nice artistic death, Kirsteen. Will you spare me now?'

'Now I think you were right because this way Doran is going to get well.'

I masked Doran.

On Monday, Doran had a rash. I looked through various books on infantile diseases. It was too early to decide whether it was chickenpox or measles or something worse. While I was dressing Lili I noticed little blisters on her knees and bottom. She escaped and sat down on the kitchen floor to mask a brain injured teddy bear.

The rash was on exactly those bodily parts that were exposed to pressure on the lino. When people arrived, Doran's crawling was motivated by a ceremonial washing down of his detergent-polluted athletic field. I agreed, for the future, to a Victorian solution of hot water and elbow grease.

My visitors were forming more predictable teams. I was beginning to tell which day of the week it was, from the sequence of faces. This almost became my way of determining whether it was morning, afternoon or evening, now that clocks only signified maskings or patternings. I was living in the programme like a spider at the centre of her web. Lili was lifted to and from play school or taken out by some of her newly found friends. The furthest I went was the garden gate to wave goodbye.

If I was short of somebody I phoned friends or the acquaintances of friends or the friends of acquaintances, or the acquaintances of acquaintances, until the gap was filled. I even pulled in passing ramblers. My aim was never to lose.

One day Kirsteen said, 'You know you'd get more help from the Steiner school if they understood why you teach Doran reading.'

'What about it?'

'They think that if children begin developing their intellect too early they will lose their spirituality.'

'But normal children are learning through their senses at such a rate and their everyday experience is very exciting. Doran's problems have restricted him so much it's important both emotionally and neurologically that he reads.'

After the next masking Diana caught me, 'I have a suggestion,' she said. 'It's only a suggestion, but I think it's a good one. Suppose one morning you come down to my shop and do your patternings there. Everyone can see what goes on, then you can answer their questions. The floor's warm, and we'd get it clean for you.'

We chose the end of the following week. Diana put up a notice and borrowed some photographs, just in case anyone still didn't know what Doran looked like.

A new team from the village arrived on Monday afternoon. Doran undertook to instruct them himself. He wriggled his arms and legs and roared with laughter. I anticipated a social victory but one of the women drew me aside, 'I can't do this; it's terrible.'

'I thought Doran was rather enjoying it,' I answered.

'Don't you think what you're doing's cruel? What time does he have to himself. It's not fair to the kiddie.'

I had never in my entire association with Doran thought of him as a 'kiddie'. I tried for a moment to see the situation through her eyes. Eventually I said, 'Would you rather he never grew up?'

'I couldn't hurt a child; I'm sorry, that's my final word.'

'So be it,' I replied, and advanced towards Doran with his mask in my hand. The other two women were on their knees encouraging him with a jack-in-the-box.

'He's doing well,' one of them remarked. 'When do you want us to come again?'

On Friday we went to Diana's to convince a large number of people that Doran could be transformed into a normal child, with the prospect of a lusty adulthood before him. We chose our best songs and wedged ourselves round a table between the dried fruit and the grains. Doran crawled behind the counter. His progress was slow, but it could already be counted in feet rather than inches. Kirsteen arrived to commence her own public relations campaign on our behalf. 'Have you met Doran yet? Come and talk to his mother.'

From time to time I showed reading cards to Doran, and waited for the customers to tell me that, in Steiner's view, children should not have the world crystallized into such a specific form as that of the written word until they were seven. 'Steiner wasn't dogmatic, so far as I know,' I said. 'Surely the situation is different in Doran's case?' To my delight I could sense that people were agreeing with me, and Doran's friendliness became even more persuasive.

When the shop closed at lunch time we had another list of names. Diana came over. 'I should say that was quite successful, but people continue to amaze me.'

'For good or bad?'

She laughed. 'Both. You had a lot of good things said about you, but one woman came up and said did I know you gave both your children strong intoxicants.'

'I don't even drink them myself. Did she claim she knew me well?'

'Oh, people who talk like that always get the information from "a friend" and when pressed they can never remember quite who.'

After the visit to Diana help looked more secure. The next day two friends rushed in with four huge wooden blocks which lifted the weight of the table and eased our backs. If I was desperate I put everyone in the car and appeared at Kirsteen's. She was always ready to call in a neighbour to make up the team. The timer on the cooker finally broke under the strain of the maskings; it was replaced by another – red, expensive and portable.

By May Doran was crawling across the kitchen floor to get to grips with an enticing plastic toy. He could use the thumb and finger of each hand in a pincer movement, but holding his bottle, or any object that required coordination of his other fingers, was still impossible. When he saw the other children playing on the swing in the garden he began trying to climb over the back step. This involved pushing up with his left knee, and was spectacular enough to warrant opening the glass doors and putting lino down outside, to tempt him to make the final effort. The spirit of the enterprise was high and had a good momentum. I was told that 'flu was about but I didn't take the rumour seriously until one or two of my visitors began to disappear. I had been giving vitamins to Doran and Lili; they had an invisible, but real, protection. The best way of averting disasters I might be threatened with seemed to be to forget them until the last possible minute. Wasn't I running on willpower which was too abstract a force to succumb to a virus?

I could tell from the faces about me that it was Wednesday. Doran was crawling to an abacus belonging to a fourteen-month-old child who was trying to pick the beads off and eat them. He eventually arrived at this goal, pushed the abacus to the floor, and began ostentatiously to teach his friend how to count.

'Well at any rate he's sliding the beads,' I said, and sneezed.

Doran did exceptionally well that day while I slowly deteriorated. I was worried, even if I could keep walking about would it be fair to ask people to come in and help at the risk of infection? I began to feel steadily weaker and resorted to doubling my intake of tea. My blood was probably the colour of P.G. Tips. When the last person had left it was about seven thirty. Doran still had a considerable amount of his floor programme left and the house was a battlefield strewn with toys, books, words, cards and masks. I crawled around beside him holding the timer and masking him at the command of its buzz. Then, in some desperation, I rang Brenda.

She offered to come immediately. The only other person who could officially coordinate the programme was Magda; while I was still vertical I called her.

'I don't suppose there's any chance you could help me? I think I've got the 'flu.'

'That's extraordinary because I've just been given two extra days' holiday; I'll come down tomorrow.'

'It's a lovely place for a holiday, as you know,' I said.

In the morning I got as far as the sofa and fell on to it. The taste in my mouth was sufficiently foul to put me off food and drink. I lay back and watched through half-closed eyelids. Doran's workforce arrived and close behind them came Magda. I guessed she must have started out very early. She assumed control and I eased back into a twilight in which I was dimly aware of Lili stroking my brow and offering cold compresses. Sometimes I could hear Doran's crawling in progress. From my own incapable state his effort appeared even more impressive. There was suddenly a lot of clapping.

'He's over the back step!'

When Sunday came I got up and had a bath. I was a nasty yellowish colour and looked as if any youth I still had had gone for ever. I noticed that the bones of my arms and legs stuck out alarmingly. Then I remembered people warning me that I must drink if I had fever to prevent dehydration. This, I concluded, must be dehydration, because I hadn't bothered to drink. Feeling rather guilty for my self neglect, I sat down with a glass of water. 'I always thought it was a joke,' I muttered, pouring myself more – 'except in the desert and in babies with kidney failure.'

Kirsteen came in the afternoon and brought me some soup; she held the bowl and seemed anxious to feed me.

'Will I ever be young or taste food again,' I asked mournfully.

Lili said, 'I think you're still very pretty, mummy.'

The room looked like the aftermath of a party; I had a longing for wild music. I pushed a heap of toys together with my foot. The bell went and Magda picked Doran up to mask him, setting the spokes of the anti-roll device on either side of her knee. I remembered the word cards; they were my duty and were the one thing he'd missed. I picked up a set and flashed them at him.

'I'm better,' I announced.

Magda and Kirsteen thought this a little premature, Kirsteen suggested acupuncture. Magda said, 'You shouldn't have to cope alone. I've heard of a charity called Community Service Volunteers. They send young graduates out to work with Institutions or families in need. How would you feel about someone else living in your house?'

'Absolute bliss!'

'Okay. I'll ring them up tomorrow morning.'

'If I hadn't caught the 'flu you two wouldn't be suggesting such superb things.'

'Go and lie down again.' They pressed me back to the sofa.

The spring was unusually warm and the garden was covered in daisies. Doran pushed himself up on his knees and elbows and squirmed over the back step. A little flurry of wind caught up a few dead leaves and whirled them towards him. He screamed and turned his head away; for a few seconds he was terrified. The wind dropped and the leaves lay still beside him; he viewed them suspiciously and backed away.

'Whatever is the matter with him?' someone asked. 'What did he see?'

I said, 'It was the leaves. He's never understood wind before. All the things he's known stay still, unless someone moves them. He thinks the leaves are alive.'

Doran went on developing his new view of the world. His height and weight had increased and his chest was broader; only his head size didn't seem to have altered appreciably. One consequence of this was a brilliant eruption of gold curls which had simply a smaller space.

The children who came to the house remembered their visits. They knew which songs they wanted to sing and chose toys to bring for Doran. The house had become a playgroup. Lili, who had at first welcomed everyone with open arms, was now less sure. She began to collect our belongings and stand guard.

'No, this is mummy's; don't touch.'

'Please Lili, don't say that; it sounds unfair, they've come to help.'

Since I'd been ill I'd become acutely aware of how dependent I was on my daughter's good nature. Lili needed to be more involved; it was no longer a game between the three of us, we had the cast of thousands. Doran was thriving on it but Lili was quite reasonably digging in her heels for a better role.

Meanwhile Magda had been in touch with Beverly Abbott, at the CSV Organization. She had found a young woman from Yorkshire called Nancy Elliott who could come down almost at once.

The day before Nancy was due, one of my friends presented me with another smaller, more practical, kitchen table. The theory was that if I moved the present patterning table into the front room, which had become a mere antechamber, we could pattern Doran on it while Nancy cooked the lunch. Two young men from the Steiner College offered to move the original table. It had been brought in a long time ago, now a new front door, plus a line of bookshelves, compromised its chances of ever getting out. They laid bets on the most likely method of success; I only intervened when they suggested chopping off its legs. Eventually they took the interior door off its hinges and by backing the table into the broom cupboard and upending it, the thing arrived at its projected location by the living room window, just as the afternoon crew were coming through the door. We had a month to go before we were due back in Philadelphia with our goal of a thousand feet.

Nancy arrived in two days. I asked a friend to pick her up from the station. Neither had any clear picture of whom they were looking for but they arrived united.

We were well into the afternoon session, singing, cheering and cajoling. I had no time to explain anything so Lili took the initiative.

'Will you read me a story, please?' She produced a book and settled herself on Nancy's knee.

Nancy was nineteen but she felt more like my big sister, which was exactly what I wanted. She had a deadpan sense of humour. I have no idea how she found out exactly what we did, but drawers and cupboards were mysteriously tidied and clothes put out in orderly piles. Lili always seemed busy, and huge appetizing meals appeared. Diana said, 'The balance has come back into your household and we're all very pleased to see you looking better.'

Nancy understood children. If Lili refused to dress she'd say, 'I shouldn't bother. I don't think you can put your arm through the sleeve either. It's much too difficult for you.' Lili would shout that it wasn't and plunge herself into her clothes.

Every evening I'd arrange the toys to create the feeling that they'd been playing all night and were just peeping out to welcome the children in the morning. It was Nancy who found me out. 'You can look at things like a child,' she said. 'I've watched the way you tidy up.'

While all this was going on, Bert was still worried about money. She came round with a huge plastic bag which she called Doran's office. It contained all matters related to his history, the fund raising and the next projected trip.

'We've two hundred pounds from your article in *Woman's Own* and another two hundred pounds from public donations. The Uckfield Lions are going to help subsidize the fare, but we still need a couple of hundred at least, to get your fees paid. We've got to work on it.'

'What had you in mind?'

'Another jumble sale because we've a lot of stuff; there's also talk of a concert.'

Two of Doran's patterners, Susan Masters and Susan Harvey, were fine musicians. They had collaborated with two colleagues to give a recital at Michael Hall, the Steiner School. Doran's future depended upon the goodwill of so many that I sometimes forgot I was his mother. I assumed Bert thought she must be his mother several times over.

'Doran belongs to the world, Bert. I suppose all children

do, but we don't often get the opportunity to reach them.'

'Just now it's taking all my effort to persuade the people of East Grinstead to come to this jumble sale, luv.'

Time was running short; every day we measured the distance Doran crawled and watched it approach eight hundred feet. He had two hundred more to go. His potential was there so long as the motivation could be found for the extra initiative. He chased children and animals and ate his way along lines of raisins, but didn't increase his footage.

Bert and Judy Blowe arranged the jumble sale and many of our friends went. They even found time to buy things for us. Lili was presented with a blue velvet dress. This was a subtle choice. The dress was her own; I had given it to the first jumble sale. I often found it hard to receive, not out of pride, because I understood how much help of all kinds Doran needed, but because of a natural impulse to want to give something back in return. I went on hoping that other families with hurt children would contact me. I had been in touch with my local 'mencap' group and suggested they come along to watch and perhaps help, but no one did.

Kirsteen must have thought similarly because when there was a radio phone-in programme on brain injury, she warned me to listen. Amid the cheers, the maskings and the loud singing, I forgot to tune in. Once the day began I was lost to everything except directing Doran towards one thousand feet of floor. At lunch time the phone rang.

'Did you hear, Linda? Did you hear what he said to me. I'm so mad. I've never been so angry.'

'The phone's heating up in my ear. What on earth happened?'

'I asked the consultant why people weren't told about the Institutes. I explained a little about Doran and do you know what he said?'

'I suppose he patted your head verbally and they cut you off.'

'Worse, he said: "These poor misguided women just wiggle their children's limbs and hope."'

I laughed despite myself. 'I see, he thought men incapable of such foolishness.'

Kirsteen wasn't up to humour yet, 'How dare he.' She spoke with the pride of her ancestral Scottish origins.

'I don't think he can have known he was speaking to Lady Macbeth,' I said.

Later that afternoon Kirsteen phoned again.

'The BBC have just asked me for the Institutes address. It seems that they have a family who want to "wriggle their child's limbs and hope". I also gave them my address and phone number so they could come down and watch how you do it!'

'As soon as possible,' I said.

The only time Doran didn't spend on his programme, he spent sleeping. If he was restless in the night I masked him until he went back to sleep. He crawled a little way across the bedroom floor in his dreams, the bedclothes went with him, transported by the structure of his anti-roll device.

He crawled onwards through the daily debris which Nancy fought back.

'Lili, is that toy stuck to the carpet? I don't think you could move it, there's special glue all over it. What a shame, it'll have to lie down there all night and be trampled on.'

Overcome with sympathy Lili would always pick it up. Doran crawled to the garden gate, and finally when Kirsteen's children ran off to the car we watched him push through it and plough down the muddy farm track that lay outside, on towards the voices and laughter that were escaping him. Nancy measured the distance. He had covered a hundred and forty feet in about ten minutes.

This was his moment of liberation and the final impetus he had needed to complete one thousand feet.

Just before we were due to leave we went to the recital. To have such beautiful music played not simply for its own sake, but also for Doran, was almost unbearable. I had the choice of being blinded by my tears or gulping them back, which was likely to be loud and disconcerting for the musicians. Diana, who was sitting behind me, passed her large red and green handkerchief.

'Keep it,' she whispered, 'I'll manage with my sleeve.'

'How could you tell?' I asked afterwards.

'I have occasional bursts of intuition.'

They raised a hundred and seven pounds. The day afterwards my mother took Lili and a couple of fortunate bears on holiday to the Isle of Wight.

We were due to leave on Saturday, just before lunch, and I saw no reason to stop the show until the last moment. I'd spent the week packing; now all that was finally needed was Doran and his anti-roll device.

When Bert arrived to take us, the last patterning was in progress.

'Is he still on the table, luv?'

I broke off singing 'This old man', to shout, 'It's okay, take the suitcase.'

We were lightly dressed. Judith had warned us that June in Philadelphia would be hot.

'What about his shoes?' asked Bert.

'He doesn't have any.'

'Doesn't he have anything that will do?'

'He has bare feet for the crawling and patterning; he didn't ever need them.'

'So long as the press don't think it's out of hardship.'

We lashed the anti-roll device to the suitcase.

'It looks like a TV aerial,' said Bert. 'I don't know what US customs will make of it.'

'Actually,' I said, 'it's a mystic sign.'

As we went out to the car some photographers turned up.

'You're off already? Can you wait while we take a photo?'

'You'll have to be quick, luv; we've a plane to catch.' Bert started the car engine.

I wound down the window and Doran pushed his arm out in a salute. Before Bert could stop me I called out, 'It sounds corny, but you can say that he went all the way to America and back in bare feet . . . because he just crawled a thousand of them!'

153

10

---✳---

WHILE WE WAITED in the departure lounge I put Doran on the carpet and masked him as if we were at home. We were arousing the curiosity of our fellow travellers. Doran had no inhibitions; he crawled into peoples' holdalls and explored their trouser legs. Some passengers tried to pretend it was all quite normal and patted him on the head murmuring, 'There's a good boy.'

Two American girls watched with unabashed interest. One of them looked directly at me and said, 'He's a cute kid, what's wrong with him?'

I knew I had my first patterners, and the only ones I needed. They sat crosslegged up at the front of the plane and spent the whole seven hours with Doran.

Kennedy airport looked familiar, even the ground staff remembered us. I had scarcely left the house and never the programme for three months; the United States was clearer in my memory than the bend in the road outside the cottage door. We were about to be waved through Customs. An officer was asking the usual questions but this time, when he was told Doran was brain injured, he frowned and searched through our passport again.

'You haven't got a visa waiver. He can't enter America without one.'

'But I had the visa from the American Embassy in London; they knew Doran's details. You must have misunderstood.'

'I don't make mistakes, lady. That child is brain injured, right?'

I nodded. He heaved out a large book and looked under

sections which dealt with the mentally disturbed.

'If he's brain injured, he's disturbed.'

I went through all the reasons I could think of which might prevent us being sent back on the next plane. At last he said, 'All right, to show you that the American people have a heart, this time I'll let you through. When you get back to England, you contact the Embassy and get that waiver.'

'Gladly, I will. Thank you.' I was anxious to leave before he changed his mind.

'What kept you?' Judith asked.

'The kind heart of the American people, thank God.'

We went down to Chestnut Hill by train. The hotel looked a little shabbier once we'd passed the restaurant and reception. We could hear children moving about on the landing. Families were filling in their hefty reports, encouraging their children to crawl and masking them to the bells of different timers. A few beer cans had already appeared on the table. Francis was explaining that he got Susan to crawl by dropping toy bombs behind her. His wife was still dressed for a chilly morning in Lancashire. It was hot outside, almost unbearably hot for the English, but her suitcase had somehow been diverted to Rome.

The Clinic was air-conditioned; inside everyone lay on the floor exchanging stories. Doran found Carla, the girl with the pretty eyes who had taken his fancy three months before. She was slimmer now and a crawler, with her own neat anti-roll device. More families had brought their other children; the Institutes appeared to have cousins, uncles and aunts as well. The Institutes staff were almost as international as their patients.

After we had been assessed, physically, intellectually and physiologically, Doran's progress was evaluated by a young Brazilian called Leia. His chest size had increased by 0.9 cm which was the same speed as a normal child, the rate of change was therefore one hundred percent. His height had increased by 2.5 cm, which made the rate of change sixty-seven percent; only his head growth remained poor, a change of a mere twenty-five percent. Nevertheless his overall growth rate was now eighty-two percent compared with sixty-three percent before we began the programme, which was excellent.

Doran also had a reading victory. Leia held up three cards at a time, starting with 'garden', 'table' and 'aeroplane'.

'In which of these did you come to America, Doran?'

His arms flew out eagerly to 'aeroplane'. He didn't make a single mistake. We were going to learn a new method of improving respiration, called 'respiratory patterning', which would be demonstrated in the lectures. Rumours travelled fast. Having experienced open house for three months, with complete strangers becoming long lost friends in a matter of hours, the shyest parent on the floor was now an extrovert. All of us had been through the fifteen patternings a day but there were considerable variations depending on individual factors. The children who could walk were walking miles, besides creeping on all fours and combat crawling. The ones who could sit up had a curious tail attached to their anti-roll devices or wore uncomfortable looking canvas bags filled with what appeared to be squashed tin cans.

The Canadian family with the deaf boy hadn't returned. It seemed that not all parents had believed the results would be worth the effort of rearranging their lives. A Spanish family had come back but had not attempted to do the programme; they were sent home. The Institutes flew a team out to Australia so the parents of the hyperactive Australian boy were spared another trip. Two children were hard to recognize. The repetitive ten year old was now a lean athletic figure, and an Italian boy whose hyperactivity had only been restrained by his father's vice-like grip, now walked obediently beside his mother. Everyone was impressed by Doran, who was crawling as far and as fast as possible.

There was a general eagerness to return to the lecture theatre. Once we had fallen into our seats with our coats and rugs, the staff surprised us by reading out our children's results; we clapped each other in the full knowledge of the blood, sweat and laughter behind those figures.

While I was standing in the heat of the sun during the break,

Anne Ball, an English staff member, caught me.

'Mrs Scotson, we've chosen Doran to demonstrate the respiratory patterning. Do you mind?'

'I'm sure he'd love it.'

'We'll bring him down during the last part of the lecture.'

The purpose of respiratory patterning was to give clear tactile information about regular breathing. To demonstrate the chaos caused by having one's breathing thrown out of pattern, volunteers ran round the lecture theatre until they were exhausted. They were then asked to eat a sandwich, sing, or recite a poem before they had regained their respiratory organization; the athletes panted loudly, proclaiming their incapacity.

Anne produced an example of one of the respiratory patterning jackets. It was a straight piece of quilted canvas which fitted under the child's armpits, reaching to just below the waist, and curving half way round the body. Three canvas straps, one and two-third inches wide, were fitted to each side; they interlocked across the chest and stretched round two wooden dowels. Anne explained that the child lay on his back on the table while two well-instructed people sat opposite each other pulling gently and evenly on the dowels to the individually determined beat of a metronome.

At this point my child was ceremoniously brought in. Doran beamed around at everybody as though he were about to make a speech; we began to stuff him into the jacket with rather less dignity. He knit his brows, his bottom lip went out, his complexion darkened. As I put my hands over my ears, he took a deep breath and howled. A ripple of unnecessary compassion on his behalf moved through the audience. Anne raised her voice in order to be heard, 'We thought this would be a treat, Doran.'

By the time the bell went for the break he had come to the conclusion that the experience was actually pleasurable; he travelled smugly back to the Clinic in Anne's arms. Two days later, when we were given Doran's own personal respiratory programme, it was I who suffered. The purpose of the exercise

157

was to improve Doran's neurological function in all areas, especially mobility; he was to have four twenty minute, and one half hour period. Anne set us up at the table with Doran laid out cheerfully between us; then she turned on the metronome. It made a sound rather like cracking a whip. I was instructed to pull, hold and release to the repetitive beat. The noise was hypnotic; I tried to seem confident but Judith could see the glazed look appearing in my eyes.

She was a musician and used to metronomes, so I followed her blindly. The whip appeared to be cracking at a variety of different speeds which had no bearing on my arm movements. I began to imagine I would go mad; I couldn't see how I could possibly go home and instruct someone else.

When we stopped I felt distinctly seasick. I smiled my thanks and was about to totter away when Anne said, 'Good. Suppose you come back every half hour and do ten minutes, then we can check the results on Doran.'

'Doran?'

I had forgotten it had anything to do with Doran. He had fallen asleep.

'He seems happy enough,' she said.

Judith assured me that my reaction was quite normal and that I would one day find no difficulty. Mercifully before we actually left the Institutes I had begun to suspect her of being right.

In between bouts of this ordeal by fire we met Janet Doman, the director of the Institute for Intellectual Excellence. Doran could already read three hundred and forty-five words at least which could now be combined in sentences, he was also to have three hundred new words a month and one homemade book a day. I digested this calmly and we passed on to a new aspect of the programme: the BITS of Intelligence.

This was to give Doran a huge amount of information and cause his brain to grow. I could see that an active child takes in hundreds of fresh facts about the world every day, the physical changes in him alter his relationship to familiar things. How could a child whose perceptions were blurred, chaotic, or non-existent collect information and make the connections necessary for creative thought? The answer looked simple; Doran was to have ten categories of ten cards, with a clear, precise unambiguous pictures glued to them; individual cards were to be seen three times a day for ten days. Each day an old category was to be exchanged for a new one. The goal for the next visit was to see eighteen hundred different 'bits'.

How would I find the material, left to my own ingenuity.

'The interesting thing,' Janet said, 'is that the "BITS" programme does literally grow kids' brains, and that changes their head size.'

She took us on to the subject of maths. The Institutes had discovered that small children could recognize large numbers represented as randomly arranged dots on a page. In the next three months Doran was going to learn addition, subtraction and division. 'And he should have a lot of fun,' said Janet. 'His goal is to enjoy maths.'

'I wish I did,' I said. 'Perhaps it's because I can't stand counting; I'm having so much trouble with the metronome.'

'Look at it as a waltz rhythm,' suggested Judith.

Rosalind found us several patternings later, 'Are you ready to get to grips with Doran's floor programme? Do you want to find out how to be a creeper, Doran?'

Doran crawled neatly into her office and she began to dictate . . .

'Remember you must react to Doran holding himself on all fours, or as we call it, in the "quad" position with the same spirit and enthusiasm as you would to metres of crawling.'

'Tape a few football crowds for him,' Judith suggested. 'Its the cricket season, I'll send Brenda to Lord's.'

'Doran is to have lots of crawling on carpet and over obstacles so you can afford to go overboard,' Rosalind smiled.

It was impossible to imagine Doran supporting himself. To give him the idea of it, he was also to have a gravitational device. This was a canvas sling on springs which supported his chest and stomach, suspending him on his hands and knees, about an inch away from the carpet. His goals were to be able to crawl a thousand feet on carpet, six hundred feet over obstacles and to hold the quad position for five minutes. He was to have two marathon days a week, when he did half the patternings and maskings and concentrated upon the crawling.

We left the Institutes late on Friday night. On the way to the airport Judith said, 'Do you know you're putting raisins in my mouth every time you put them in Doran's?'

'Never.'

'You've been doing it for the last fifty miles. They were very pleasant.'

We came home to be mothered by Nancy. Brenda made the respiratory jacket while another friend rigged up the sling, called a 'turtle', under the work table to save space.

Volunteers made obstacles out of sandbags covered in striped deck chair material. These were distributed throughout the house but persuading Doran to climb over them was hard. The doorstep had been baited with the incentive of the great outside world, whereas the sight of yet another obstacle ahead appeared poor reward for his effort. I began to sound like a sports commentator and when Lili came home from my mother's she competed with her brother in a daily steeple-chase. We still had to get through ten patternings and sixty maskings, plus the respiratory patternings and the intelligence programme.

When I first told Nancy about the 'bits' cards she went off to the nearest junk shop and came back with a stack of old postcards of birds of prey and scenic views of America. The 'bits' appealed to people. They meant that the things one didn't want to throw out but couldn't justify keeping could be redeemed for good use. In between patternings some friends sorted, cut and glued cards while others labelled them neatly on the back.

'Doran,' I would enthuse, 'look – ten American presidents.' (Or ten Egyptian monuments, or ten battleships. . . .)

Doran's attention was riveted; his eyes widened. I slaughtered books of paintings on his behalf.

As our schedule got tighter we ate our meals from upturned plastic bread trays (loaned as obstacles) and sat round the turtle, while Doran ate his actually in the turtle. He bounced back and forth in between mouthfuls, maintaining his famous healthy appetite and robust digestion.

In the middle of one of these meals Bert turned up with Doran's office in a plastic bag. She spread out her stuff on top of the table and I handed her some rice and salad.

'Do you want a chair?'

'No thanks, luv, I'd rather stand. I'm in a hurry as always. You realize we have no money?'

'I know. I was waiting for my unconscious mind to send up a good idea.'

'We need a lot of money, Linda.'

Doran bobbed towards his plate and took a mouthful of dinner.

'His programme's so entertaining,' I said, 'we could charge for performances.'

'We need something like a sponsored walk.'

'Couldn't we have people sponsor Doran to make his goals?'

'We need to be more public, luv.'

'How about sponsoring someone else to do his programme?'

Bert's eyes lit up. 'That's it – I've got the idea. A sponsored crawl.'

'Bert, that's brilliant.'

She swallowed the rest of her dinner.

'I'm going round to Judy Blowe's. I'll see how she likes the idea. Bye now.' She bent down under the table, 'Bye, Doran. Keep up the good work, boy.'

There was another fund raiser at large. Jane Stimson, one of the first people who had come to help Doran, suggested the 'Thousand Club'. It meant that if a thousand people could be persuaded to pay a pound each every time Doran went to America, we'd have enough to cover most of our costs. There was a large sweet jar in her hall for collecting any small change left in the pockets of parting guests. (Diana kept a similar jar in her shop into which she invited customers to put donations.)

Meanwhile although Doran struggled over his sandbags and crawled with increasing vigour across the floor, he showed no signs of 'quading'. I wondered if anybody believed he was capable of achieving this goal. However impossible it seemed, I accepted the fact that sooner or later it would happen.

As the summer moved on, people went on their holidays and I appealed for others to fill the gaps. We had too complicated a programme now to decamp to Kirsteen's, so we advertised in the village.

I knew the first two people to come were both interested in Rudolph Steiner's philosophy, and I hoped there would be a good deal of common ground between us. Half way through the afternoon a slight tension in the atmosphere made me ask the younger woman how she felt.

'I think you're destroying Doran's spiritual purpose. Children like him have a reason to be like they are. I don't believe you understand it.'

'Can't you see it's no fun being brain injured? Doran doesn't want to be crippled. He may benefit from having had the experience but it wasn't intended to be permanent, any more than if he broke his leg.'

She put out her hand. 'I'm not saying you don't want to do your best for Doran, I'm sure you do, but I couldn't do this and be at peace with myself.'

She left to walk up the road. Her friend had such a sympathetic face. I said, 'What can I do? She believes something I don't; I respect her argument but it hurts me.'

'I think she had her mind made up before she arrived. Don't worry, I'll help you.'

She came throughout the summer and on into the following year.

News of the sponsored crawl spread, and we decided to combine it with a 'Summer Fayre' at the playing fields in East Grinstead. Diana elected to crawl. She put up a notice to that effect in her shop.

'. . . and a pound of tomatoes? And, have you heard, I'm crawling for Doran? Would you like a sponsor form?'

How could anyone refuse?

Bert had a habit of appearing, emptying her office on to the table, making a few hectic notes and vanishing in the space of ten minutes. As the crawl grew nearer these manifestations became more frequent.

'People started by thinking we meant swimming, luv.'

'"The crawl" rather than "a" crawl?'

'So we've had to put them in the picture. Actually, it's a sponsored "creep". We can't very well have people down on their stomachs.'

No one came to the house without being allotted a job. Bert had lists of names covered in ticks and crosses. 'Dad asks my permission to use his phone; that's how tough it is,' she said.

The glorious spring weather had developed into rain and cloud with sunny periods; we booked the gym hall as well as the field. Diana secretly practised creeping round her garden. Magda was coming and Moe had promsied to take photographs. It was Doran's marathon day; the forecast was bad and Bert was not happy, but this was England so she said, 'We can only hope things might buck up.'

Doran worked through his Saturday morning routine, oblivious of the rain, and the delicate balances on which his future rested. At 1.30 p.m. we arrived at the site, paddled past a small travelling fair, its awnings dripping with water, and put Doran down on the most spacious floor he'd ever seen. Lili wanted to ride on the roundabout but Nancy suggested we find Magda first. The hall was full of merchandise and stall holders who knew Doran either by sight or through the newspapers; all they lacked were customers.

'What else have people to do on a miserable afternoon?' I asked.

'Go to the pictures, or better still, watch the telly,' Bert sighed.

Two of the older children volunteered to dress up in costumes borrowed from the Summer Fayre to go and enlighten anyone in the High Street and drag them back. The crawlers had started arriving complete with their own individual fancy dress, knee pads and gloves. Doran was doing very well on his own.

'Bert,' I said, 'couldn't they go round the outside of the hall? It would look quite exciting.'

'That's not what it would feel like. Doran's a seasoned crawler; they'd only manage a couple of laps and collapse. That floor is hard.'

I sighed. Bert went on. 'I'm not pouring cold water on your idea but distance means money.'

She was called away by Judy who had noticed a group of strangers and was tempted to believe they might be consumers. They were actually a team from the National Childbirth Trust with a large box of home-made cakes. Magda was following Doran so I began looking for Nancy and Lili. When I was sure they weren't in the hall I tried outside. The ground was still very muddy but there was a small patch of blue in the grey clouds. I watched it getting bigger and heading our way. Lili was singing on the merry-go-round; she was its only customer but a trickle of women and children were approaching from the direction of the town. Nancy was supervising Lili.

'It's brightening up,' she said. 'Are they going to crawl? Once they start they won't mind a bit of rain. It's quite warmish.'

I rushed off to find Bert.

'They must get started, look at the weather.'

'The field's very wet, it's lunatic enough on a good day.' At this point Diana arrived dressed as a tortoise with a line of would-be crawlers behind her.

'When are we going to start?' she asked.

'We want to crawl! We want to crawl!' chanted her retinue.

Judy Blowe and Bert's father departed to set up the course. By now there was bright sunlight, the little fair had perked up and small customers were now revolving on the backs of giraffes and horses.

The ground was soft enough not to destroy kneecaps and the contestants managed more laps than any of their sponsors could have predicted. Diana raised over two hundred pounds.

Despite all this glory, Doran was still as incapable of "quad-ing" as the first day we'd attempted to introduce it. He could certainly surmount bigger, more interesting obstacles and crawl a thousand feet over carpet, but if he couldn't quad, the possibility of his ever balancing on two feet looked remote. I knew we had to postpone our visit to the Institutes until Doran reached his goals. I made myself accept this as inevitable; at the same time I aimed for the impossible.

'Doran, for God's sake stiffen up!'

Doran ignored me and crumpled back on to his stomach.

'He's tired,' someone said. 'Could he have a drink?'

I didn't think Doran was tired, but I accepted the excuse and gave her the bottle. She took him into the garden. In a few seconds I heard her call, 'Did Doran ever hold his own bottle?'

'No, you have to. He doesn't open his fingers properly.'

'Well, he does now.'

Doran was lying on his back in her arms clutching the bottle with both hands and sucking intently. Every so often he would remove the teat from his mouth, grin and thrust it back again.

There were other changes noticeable in Doran once I stopped being obsessional about his inability to quad. His head looked bigger. Janet had predicted that new information would enable the brain to grow and if the brain grew, the skull would grow to fit it . . . He looked taller and when he turned his gaze on you, from time to time both his pupils would simultaneously move in your direction; Doran was converging.

When I phoned Rosalind at the Institutes, her interest lay in Doran's crawling record. The implication was that if he achieved his floor goal and still wasn't up on all fours, they needed to find some other way of putting him there. She was anxious to reevaluate him.

I didn't think of the seasons any more, or of the time going by. I measured my life in visits to the Clinic. When people asked what date it was we went back, I said 'the twenty second', expecting them to know which month as though September was marked in red in everyone's calendar. The twenty-third would be Doran's third birthday. Magda had decided to come with us again, but this time she wanted to stay on a few days to study the Institutes human development course.

Doran pushed on up hill and down dale, over more and more obstacles. As he worked, his knees began to flex underneath him and I had the first hint of what it might be like to see him free of the ground. I was sitting down cutting out 'bits' with Nancy late one evening, when she said, 'Do you think Doran's talking? I do, but I wouldn't admit to it.'

'To my mind he goes on about a lot of things. He really grumbles well.'

A week before we were due back in Philadelphia, he was on the edge of reaching his target.

I contacted Rosalind who had a way of giving me the determination to make the final push.

'Doran sounds great, but he must make his floor goals. We look forward to seeing you.'

We lined the track as if it were the Grand National and we'd staked all our investments on one horse. The horse made it, but I lost my voice.

When my mother came to collect her for her own holiday, Lili said, 'Mummy, how will you tell them about Doran in America if you can't speak?'

'I hope he'll do the talking,' I whispered.

A local organization decided to raise funds for a charity; they had chosen Doran and the East Grinstead Boxing Association. This seemed an implausible combination but we were very grateful. Doran was to appear at their garden fête as the guest of honour a few hours before we flew out. Nancy left a day before us, accepting a lift back to Yorkshire, but a succession of friends appeared on Saturday morning to help push Doran over a few final obstacles. Unlike my last orderly departure, the front room was strewn with books, notes and clothes. No one could believe the jigsaw would fit into place. When a neighbour offered to drive into the village and buy anything I wanted, I remembered there were actually things I did still want.

I was going to leave my car at Kirsteen's where Diana had promised to pick us up. I saw her van parked outside the gate with its occupant slumped over the wheel. Diana was fast asleep. When I knocked on the window she jumped up. Her face looked red and swollen.

'I just closed my eyes,' she said.

'Diana, you were out and by the look of you, you've the most appalling cold.'

She sneezed into her handkerchief.

'It's beastly, but if you sit in the back you won't catch it.'

We reached the gateway of the large country house where the fête was taking place to find a piper, resplendent in kilt and sporran, waiting to pipe us along the drive while Doran stuck his head and shoulders out of the window to acknowledge the cheering.

We met Magda at the airport; slowly the smell of the English autumn faded. When the plane landed at Kennedy the visa waiver worked and Doran, Magda and I were soon back with Judith in our air-conditioned room at the Chestnut Hill Hotel.

Rosalind went over Doran's progress early on Monday morning. Not only had Doran made his floor goal but he had surmounted obstacles higher and nearer together than she had intended.

'Mrs Scotson, we like to make things tough for our kids but this is outrageous. Congratulations Doran.'

Doran stared her in the eye, his convergence was now functional. He had made a profile change in his manual ability and he had a language victory. His head had grown at twenty percent above the average rate for a two year old.

'We expect that when a kid starts on the "bits" programme but Doran's done exceptionally well . . . Last month you were worried that he wasn't making his goals, today he's a star.'

'And tomorrow it's his birthday,' said Judith.

'I see, well it's his lucky day. You break off lectures at lunch time so you can take him off and have fun.'

Judith and Magda planned a trip round old Philadelphia but the more action packed the itinerary became, the less it seemed like my idea of fun.

'What would you like to do as your treat?' Magda asked.

'Sleep.'

They left me in a state of beatific happiness in a darkened room with hours and hours of sleep before me.

The trio had no misadventures other than being incapable of putting on Doran's nappy so that he didn't pee out of the side. They were amused that with his curls and pink trousers, he was mistaken for a girl.

On Friday we faced Rosalind for the floor programme.

'This time,' she said, 'we intend to make Doran a confirmed creeper.' He was to maintain four thirty minute respiratory patternings and eight cross patternings. We had to build an open sided box or trough, which would give him lateral support so that he could balance in it in the creep position. On regular days he had to crawl two hundred and fifty feet non-stop and three hundred feet over obstacles. There were three marathon days a week and his goal for the interim report was to crawl one thousand three hundred feet on marathon days, six hundred feet non-stop and seven hundred feet over obstacles. The goal for the return visit was to creep two hundred metres on a marathon day.

'We're going to get Doran ready for walking by standing him against an inclined ladder,' Ros said. 'He'll also find it an aid to creeping.'

More details had to be recorded before we left her office. The intelligence programme sounded unusually vast, but Doran would have long periods in the trough which would be a golden opportunity for showing cards.

Many things lay disconnected on the surface of my mind; I needed to be home to find the cohesion. Magda was given a room at the Institutes and a track suit for participating in the human development course.

I checked my flight number for the tenth time. It left at

10.30 p.m. which was later than I would have liked, but it gave us time to have a meal in New York. When we took our last walk on Chestnut Hill, there was a street fair and an old fashioned brass band.

Michael had an impulse to verify the tickets; he looked unhappy.

'Linda, the flight number doesn't make sense. Either it's wrong or the time's wrong.'

I didn't understand. The tickets were sent direct from Laker and I assumed they wouldn't make a mistake. Judith took the tickets. From the number it was the 7.30 flight. They'd evidently travelled enough to make a numerical connection that escaped me. We tried to phone the airport but were granted only an answering phone.

'If we go and get the car now we may just make it. Remember you have to check in an hour early.'

Michael took Doran and we ran back blindly through the crowds. I had some vision of never getting home, but of being carried forever in a kind of paralysing dream. Hours later we reached the outskirts of New York. Michael phoned several times from a series of call boxes. When he did get through, our chances of reaching Kennedy by 7.30 were slim.

He came back looking grim.

'You had the wrong time and there's no room on the 10.30 flight.' I tried to look brave. 'But since all flights have been delayed the 7.30 flight isn't going out until 10.30, so where shall we go for supper?'

11

---✳︎---

DORAN AND I SLEPT through the first morning home while people arrived and tiptoed away. After lunch they stayed to entertain Doran and I went through my notes, posting the new programme on my walls in time for my next volunteer, Cathy, who was due to come in the late afternoon.

Peter agreed to build a version of the quad box and a stepladder for Doran to stand on. Cathy, a slim serious young woman, had a degree in maths and French and had just graduated from Teacher Training College. She was rapidly engulfed by the exuberance and chaos of the programme. By 9 p.m. we were surrounded by its debris.

'Who tidies up?' she asked, picking her way through towards the bathroom.

'We do,' I said, as I poured water over Doran and scrubbed Lili's back.

'Where does everything go?'

'Mostly in the toy box.'

Cathy took refuge in reserve.

When Lili came home she was unused to Cathy's gentle but direct discipline and began to invent a little comedy of her own which entailed being apparently helpless.

'Lili, will you put on your shoes.'

'They don't fit.'

'You wore them perfectly well yesterday.'

'Try the Cinderella's slipper approach,' I suggested and turned to my daughter, 'If the shoes don't fit, the prince will be brokenhearted.'

Lili extended her feet and the day got underway. Cathy

found herself swept to right and left as Doran switched from one activity to another with furious excitement, until he was finally launched into his pyjamas and anti-roll device, ready to be tucked up on the bedroom floor. Since the vacuum cleaner was taking an extended holiday at the electrical repair shop, until I could afford to redeem it, Cathy spent the rest of the evening brushing the floor.

Magda came down the following weekend and while Doran climbed over his line of upturned bread trays down the garden, she sat in the kitchen answering Cathy's questions. The next time I saw Cathy she looked relaxed and smiling. After Magda had left she said, 'This has been the most confusing week of my life, but at last I know what's going on.' Now that Cathy knew what she was doing she did it very efficiently.

Her calligraphy was the clearest I'd ever seen. She wrote out programmes of information, and the names on the back of the 'bits' cards with lightning speed. Judith sent packets of material from America. We would never have learnt there were so many different breeds of dog if it hadn't been for her.

I jammed Doran into his quad box with a patchwork anti-sit pack behind him; once there he ate raisins and listened to my dramatic renderings of the titles of his cards. Cathy, and sometimes Lili, held his bottom to steady him. He was prepared to push himself backwards and forwards in the turtle for a glimpse of his own resolute face in the mirror, and even more willing to stand against the vertical ladder to pose as a promisingly upright young man. Cathy was usually found in various positions of temporary safety, including crosslegged on the patterning table, behind a stack of magazines, selecting her next ten 'bits'. She had taught Lili how to cut out, her pupil was now creative and prolific. Heaps of confetti rose round the chair legs, while Lili experimented at making the smallest divisions possible with her scissors.

Doran's improvement didn't pass unnoticed by my doctor. He was anxious to have him monitored and suggested contacting a consultant from Guy's, who had just moved to the cerebral palsy hospital.

An appointment was made. I invited a friend, a trained physiotherapist called Jean who owned a small farm, and often brought Doran eggs and cream when she came to pattern him. On the way Jean told us that she had been depressed by a television programme which commented on the isolation of a group of mothers with handicapped children who were now trying to baby-sit for each other.

We were welcomed quite warmly by our original physio. I waited for her to refer to the fact that Doran was crawling along the corridor beside us, but she disappeared. Nevertheless Doran's mobility was impressive; he had new high topped boots, and he enjoyed the tough sound they made against the floor. Our physio returned to say that the doctor thought his room would be too small to accommodate all of us.

'My friends are very involved with Doran; it's important to me that they stay.'

'The doctor thinks it would be a bit of a squash that's all.'

'They've come a long way and I'm not prepared to do without them.'

After further consultation we were all allowed to troop in after her. The room was enormous; there was a surplus of chairs. We shook hands. The doctor ignored Doran who crawled off into a corner to investigate a pile of books.

'We were just talking about a jolly good television programme yesterday,' he said.

'The one about the mothers of brain injured children sitting in with each other's kids to give each of them a break?'

'Yes,' he said, 'so nice to see people making such a good effort to get out.'

I said, 'But what about the children? How did it help them?'

'I thought it indicated how dreadfully demoralized those women were,' said Jean.

The doctor changed his subject.

'So what can I do for you, Mrs Scotson?'

'I'm pleased you've offered to monitor Doran in order to get some insight into the Institutes' treatment principles.'

'I'm afraid I can't discover anything by monitoring one child.'

'But it will at least give you some personal understanding of their work.'

'Mrs Scotson, I feel I must tell you I've just come back from an American hospital; the consultant personally took me to see a lot of children whom the Institutes had failed and who had turned back to more orthodox treatment.'

'How many did you see?'

He paused, so I pressed him. 'Fifty? Twenty, ten, five?'

'Four or five.'

'And what was wrong with these four – or five?'

He couldn't remember.

'Of course,' said Jean, 'you would only see the failures because the successes wouldn't need you any more.'

'We feel justified in saying that we can get children as well as the Institutes.'

'Do your children ever walk out of here fit and well?'

'The Institutes have no means of telling that the number of their so-called successes wouldn't have got well anyway.'

'Have you ever seen a seriously brain injured child recover?'

'Mrs Scotson, I'm afraid I cannot monitor your son unless you accept our treatment methods.'

'But if I did that I would have to compromise Doran's programme and it would be even less possible for you to assess whether it was your approach or their approach which was successful.'

'Then you admit we have an approach?'

'I do, but in my experience it's not been helpful.'

'Well,' he said, 'you needn't make up your mind now. Go home and think about it.'

'Don't you even want to look at Doran?'

'It's no use my examining Doran unless I am going to treat him.'

'I think there has been some confusion about this visit,' I said, 'and since we don't see eye to eye on the matter we had better leave the situation as it stands. Good afternoon.'

When we got outside Cathy exploded, 'He wouldn't even ask how Doran was and he didn't answer any of your questions.'

'You kept very calm, Linda,' said Jean.

'I'm used to it. Look at these wonderful corridors, they're perfect for crawling along, but all the kids here are in wheelchairs or on crutches.'

'Could we find Doran a place like this on his marathon days?' Cathy reflected.

So the one good thing that came out of the visit was that Doran and I began to spend marathon days in close contact with other people's floors. I had never observed the carpets more minutely. I discovered the historic remains that vacuum cleaners don't pick up. We crawled behind sofas and in and out of bedrooms; Doran rattled through cats' saucers and skirted round dog baskets. One huge house had a long sweeping staircase which took the place of obstacles. I pushed Doran upstairs and held him as he clambered down. Lili slid from top to bottom on her stomach. When we got back he went straight onto the table for respiratory patterning while she ate tea and warmed her toes.

Doran's meals were more difficult. He resented the mushy non-adult quality of much of his food. When I gave in to him, chopping nothing, he couldn't chew successfully without spending hours on each mouthful and would have been all day eating instead of crawling. I began to make little rissole-like balls which could be thrown into his mouth if he opened it to laugh or complain. This was not wholly satisfactory.

Then Diana lent us a large rustic looking highchair she had kept for her grandchild. Doran was just supple enough to sit in it with a few cushions to counteract slumping. He was now free and willing to feed himself such things as bread and cheese.

Diana also brought us extra food and herbal tonics. One day she asked, 'When did you last paint?'

'When Doran was in hospital. Why?'

'I thought I'd enrol you with an art group at the school; I'd put Doran to bed and babysit for you.'

'Diana you're good at sounding out my heart but just now

174

it's better if you paint for me. You go to the art class?' So Diana went to the classes and began to talk to me about painting.

Doran couldn't control a crayon but he had a strong feeling for painting. He pressed other people to draw for him by persistently handing back the implements and pointing to the paper.

One afternoon a man came to mend the boiler. Doran quaded in his box watching him sort through his tools and unscrew pipes. The plumber began to explain each stage of his work; five minutes went by then ten minutes. By the time the job was done Doran had supported himself for nearly twenty-five minutes. The following Saturday was a marathon day; my friend Hilary had an ideal house, it was three cottages knocked into one. She also owned a white grand piano and a sumptuous white-tiled bathroom. Lili plus a great deal of soap and bath salts usually found a way into the bath, while Doran crawled inquisitively from the television in the kitchen to the distant sound of a keyboard from the other end of the house. He had just completed his afternoon session, I was collecting up a long trail of dolls and bears when Hilary called urgently from the kitchen. I hadn't heard any breaking glass but the voice suggested an accident. She caught me by the shoulder as I rushed in.

'Wait, look!'

Doran had wanted to watch the television and in order not to get a crick in the neck while he was doing it, he was quading independently.

'I can't believe it,' I said.

'Nor can I.'

We froze against each other, afraid that a sudden movement would startle him. After about two minutes he collapsed.

That evening Doran capitalized on his new ability. He crawled over to the bookshelves and lifted himself high enough to remove every single book. Instead of protesting, Cathy and I pulled up chairs to watch.

Lili climbed on to my knee. 'Doran's making an awful mess, mummy.'

'Yes, isn't it wonderful?'

Doran had the power to change his environment; many things which were 'up' could now be brought 'down'. He was also beginning to make new connections. Cathy had produced some beautiful cards on snow from a pile of *National Geographic* magazines. We had just started lunch when he pushed aside his bowl to gesticulate dramatically towards the window. I saw that outside the snow really had begun to fall. Doran looked as if he would like to write a scientific paper on the subject and demanded to be carried to the door and held out to catch the flakes. The snow revealed a new aspect of Cathy. She exclaimed, 'It's like a poem' and ran across the lawn without a coat, whirling happily through the white veils which had bewitched her. Cathy had anticipated staying until February, but she wanted to teach and steadily applied for all the available situations.

An answer came from Maidstone to invite her to an interview, and she was given the job which began with the January term. She decided to write to CSV explaining very precisely what the problems were and outline the kind of person who'd be most suitable as a replacement. A kind of Renaissance Woman who was as practical as she was intellectual, whose humour was as inspiring as her dedication. 'Or the next best thing, just in case she doesn't exist,' I said.

We were already patterning to Christmas carols. My mother sent two advent calendars which became an incentive for good behaviour. The possibility of not being able to open one's door brought instant cooperation from Lili and from Doran. As Christmas drew nearer, CSV phoned to say that the prospects of finding anyone who could come before Christmas were remote. Kirsteen had suggested we move the programme to her on Christmas Day; Diana invited us on Boxing Day.

I'd had a letter from Judith telling me that she was trying to find a student from Vermont who might come for a month, but since there was no further news I assumed she'd failed. So, I put a notice up in Diana's shop asking for temporary help to tide me over after Cathy left. After several unsuccessful replies I had another phone call.

'Hi, this is Emily.'

I assumed she was an American student from Emerson College.

'Shall I come over Saturday?' she went on.

'Yes, fine. Where are you now?' I said, wondering if she'd like a lift in from the village.

'I'm in a restaurant in New York City.'

Before I could ask any more her money ran out. I had no surname and no address.

We woke up on Saturday morning to find there was no electricity. The Board couldn't say when it would be corrected. Having dug out the primus stove and candles, I checked with the airport. There was only one flight in from New York that morning and Emily wasn't on it, so with a clear conscience we departed to Hilary's. She'd been unaffected by the fault and her house was full of light and warmth, which was more than usually welcome. I went straight down on my hands and knees. I could no longer imagine what it must be like to walk upright in her house or to sit in a chair with a cup of tea. That night a storm raged. There was still no electricity and no news of Emily. I was beginning to wonder if the phone call was a hoax.

On Sunday afternoon a taxi drew up outside.

'Emily!' said Lili, who'd never ceased to believe in her. Emily strode into the room and collapsed; she looked beautiful, tough and tired.

'I lost your telephone number and I had to phone my mother in Long Island for the address. It was the *worst*!'

She refused all offers of food and drink and asked to be directed to a bed. Cathy chaperoned her carefully upstairs and we left her to sleep.

By Monday afternoon we were looking in every half hour to ensure she was still alive. On Tuesday morning, we wondered if she was in danger of dehydration. Just after supper she emerged looking ravenously hungry. I piled food in front of her.

'This is the *best!*' she said, slapping her knee and jumping out of her chair to reach for more. The startling thing about Emily was that Judith had told her what to expect, and in such a way that the reality was no shock.

We went over the daily schedule scattering copious notes. Cathy explained the system of the cards, but Emily wanted to start at once. She leapt over to where the action was.

'You're doing great Doran. UP! UP! UP!'

As he clambered over the bread basket towards her, I began to wonder if I was in England or America.

The evening Cathy left we decorated the house and the 'tree', which was a firbough from the forest. Diana came round with a box full of stars, little toys and candles. When we lit the candles and turned off the light Doran had his first experience of the way in which a familiar room can become enchanted.

'Cor,' he said, pointing towards the tree. 'Cor, cor, cor!'

That evening Cathy's parents collected her, and the next day Emily's rule began.

On Christmas morning parcels gathered round the tree. Our friend Bridget who worked with Diana came early to do a respiratory patterning before we went off to Kirsteen's. It was not the most peaceful patterning of Doran's career. Emily helped him open his presents and admire Lili's, the centrepiece of which was a Wetsy Betsy from another godfather, Peter Marinker. Over the sounds of tearing paper and happiness Bridget and I followed the steady beat of the metronome.

'It's wonderful the way you call it "spiritual patterning",' Emily said afterwards.

'In a sense breath is spiritual,' Bridget answered. Emily was not enlightened, she continued to use the wrong word with poetic innocence.

Kirsteen negotiated Christmas Day as though the programme was one of its rituals. Doran crawled down channels of toys for slices of cake. Since he had three children and a cat to chase or follow, it was to his credit that he managed to squeeze his anti-roll device round the tree several times without getting it stuck. After the last mince pies were handed out, he settled down in the Noah's Ark, fast asleep but still chewing on fragments of wholemeal pastry.

Diana's house was crowded with happy people whose spontaneous outbursts of song were accompanied by lively music from the piano. After lunch Doran and I toured the upstairs rooms ending with the bathroom. He approached the bath eagerly, as he reached the side he rose on to all fours and leapt for it.

The manoeuvre was successful; he found himself standing upright beside the taps. By the time Diana appeared I'd filled the bath with water and was throwing in everything floatable. Doran began his ninth trot, each time his confidence increased, he steadied himself a little better. . . .

'Diana you have a "first" in your bathroom! Watch.'

Doran proudly crawled faster, pushed himself up, broke into a short gallop, grabbed the side and stood erect. Then he reached out for a bobbing plastic duck.

'That's creeping, Diana. It's lucky you still like playing with ducks.'

'They are quite useful for my grandchildren too,' she said.

Everyone came upstairs to see Doran creep. Diana brought him something sticky and forbidden.

'You enjoy it, my lad; I never thought I'd be proud to call anyone a "creeper" but we live and learn.'

We arrived home late, Lili was already asleep but Doran still clung to the festivities of the day. I put him on the sofa and let him count railway engines, Venetian glass, beetles, famous inventors and impressionist paintings. After the last Renoir he dozed off with visions of beautiful women in springtime.

The next day Doran solved the problem of finding an equivalent to the side of Diana's bath. He decided he was capable of climbing on to the sofa. The further we put him away the more ground he covered by creeping. He needed space. The most dynamic environment we could think of was the Felbridge Hotel Roller Disco. We were permitted to use this Mecca of floral carpets and flashing lights in the afternoons before opening time.

The tables could easily be moved into small encampments which Doran crept round or crawled through. When he had done well we turned them upside down to make sledges and whirled Doran recklessly across the floor. Children from the neighbourhood collected on the steps to peer at us through the glass doors.

One day Doran sat back on his haunches liberating his arms from the floor.

'That's incredible,' said Emily.

'Yes,' I said. 'Now we've got to stop him doing it.'

Sitting, like rolling, was a neurological dead end and the Institutes had given us a good name for this particular choice of position.

'Just in case you're tempted to admire it, Emily, it's called the "God Awful".'

'Why?'

'It deforms the hip joints and curves the spine. Let's try his anti-sit.' Unfortunately the cushion which we had used to wedge him into the now obsolete trough was useless out of it. We tried adding a number of squashed tin cans but he was more interested in their rattle behind him than a creeping goal ahead. A friend of Magda's decided to make a prototype. She arrived with a shining curved cruxiform that looked like a prop from a science fiction movie. It had a long polished tail and a black harness. The problem was that it needed four feet of space for its wearer to turn round. Since that didn't exist, except in fields, we hung it on the wall to wait for the weather to improve.

Bert and Judy raised money from the Christmas bazaar and raffle, and Jane Stimson had been steadily fund-raising through the thousand club. There would be no panic getting Doran to the Institutes by March. Besides this Hilary had decided I'd need physical as well as financial support and was coming with us.

'I'll do your laundry,' she said. 'You're to be packed a week

in advance. In fact I think I'll start taking your clothes now.'
She went away with a bundle of dresses and the determined
look of a Spanish washerwoman.

CSV did send me another volunteer but not the Renaissance
Woman of my dreams. She was from another culture; I tried
to guide her.

'You will not make Lili more cooperative if you threaten to
burn down her dolls house . . . The problem with this routine
is it never stops.'

Somehow she couldn't get started.

When Emily went to London for New Year's Eve all I could
offer my companion was further idleness, a bottle of Mateus
Rosé and conversation, while I cleaned up and made cards.
When she had finished the bottle she said goodnight and went
to bed. It was arguably the worse New Year's Eve of her life.

In the morning over breakfast she leant forward earnestly.
'I don't know how to tell you this but I can't stay here any
longer. It's your daughter; I can't control your daughter.'

I didn't stand in her way and she left before lunch. Doran,
Lili, the Wetsy Betsy and I went to Hilary's for a marathon.
By the time we arrived there I was bursting to dance round
the kitchen.

'Hilary, it's awful of me but I'm so happy. She really wanted
to go; it's a lovely, lovely feeling. How did Lili do it?'

'What did I do, mummy?'

'I don't know, angel; most people find you irresistible.'

Lili went off to show her Wetsy Betsy to Hilary's nineteen-
year-old son who was at that moment playing poker with some
old school friends.

CSV resumed the search; their deadline was Valentine's Day
when Emily was booked to fly home.

Without a CSV I was saving a little money. Peter suggested
I should spend it finding a way of reducing the damp on the
wall by the front door. Doran's creeping became more realistic
but with no adequate anti-sit device someone had to be constantly behind him to prevent the tempting bunny hops. The
only thing Emily couldn't do well was to actually write on the

cards – her calligraphy appeared almost illegible. I couldn't replace Cathy's style, but Judith arrived home. She patiently devoted every free moment to making 'bits'. Doran stood with his arms stretched up to reach the rungs of a ladder balanced between the patterning table and the bookshelves so I sat underneath the table showing him the cards. As long as the pictures kept coming, Doran kept standing. One day I banged my head on the bottom of the table and moved back to protect myself. Doran moved forward. He took a complete step using his hands on the rungs to steady him. I backed further away; he took another step. I leaned forward to embrace him hitting my head harder and noticing less. Doran realized what he'd done and fell off in surprise. Nevertheless he had convinced all those present that he would one day walk.

From about this time Doran refused to crawl. He had a new goal ahead of him, to complete two hundred yards of creeping in one day. Usually Emily reserved the word 'great' for Doran's mobility and 'the worst' for his nappies. As if to oblige her distaste he became increasingly constipated. After I had tried all the more common purgatives, I was given a homeopathic remedy which involved dipping hot towels in camomile tea and wrapping them around his stomach. Doran bore this with great fortitude. Nevertheless I had to resort to using my fingers for the final delivery – while Doran bent over my knee, and Emily and Lili held his hands.

'That,' said Emily, as delight and relief suffused Doran's face, 'was the *worst*.'

'Followed,' I said, 'thank God, by the "best". He's gone to sleep.'

By the beginning of February it was not unreasonable to worry about who was coming next. The demands I had now made on the candidate were perhaps a little excessive but I hoped some part at least was realistically possible.

After raising and dashing my hopes a couple of times, CSV suggested a biology graduate called Alison Geddes who was waiting to travel to the tropical rain forest to do research for a Ph.D. The woman who interviewed her told me that Alison was the most unusual person she'd ever met but didn't explain why. The letter I had about her told me she liked sport and had been working as an office clerk to save money. She was willing to come on the seventh. Emily said, 'She'll be tall and slender with straight fair hair and glasses.'

The seventh happened to be the day Peter had decided to put wood over the living room wall to reduce the damp. He moved all the furniture to the middle of the room, Doran made a figure of eight round it, passing Lili who sat drawing passionately at the kitchen table, oblivious to everything but the next sheet of paper.

There was a knock at the door, I shouted, 'Come in', but that was impossible. Alison's actual entry had to be preceded by a grand removal of furniture, tongue and groove boarding and boxes of nails.

She had short brown hair; I noticed a gold ear-ring in her ear. She wasn't tall but she bounced with highly compressed energy. Everybody spoke at once. When Alison did sit down she said, 'Doran looks very normal.'

'Apart from being brain injured, he's completely normal,' I said.

'Doran's a genius,' Emily explained.

Then Lili ran in with a book, 'Read me a story.' I induced Doran to continue creeping, with my foot behind him to prevent bunny hops. After the story I could hear Emily and Alison talking about biology and feminism. As I listened, I concluded, I've struck it lucky, this woman thinks!

That evening I began persuading her to believe in the logic behind the programme. 'You have to consider the brain as a computer,' I said, while I shampooed Lili's hair with one hand and held Doran's head out of the water with the other. 'Doran, you may not swallow the entire bath. Without input there cannot be output, chaotic input means chaotic output.'

I let go of Doran to rinse the hair; he screamed joyously thrashing waves over all of us and the bottle of shampoo into the adjacent toilet basin.

'Without the right sensory input,' I said, retrieving the

bottle and closing the toilet lid, 'you can't expect the correct motor output.'

Alison was unused to her lectures being punctuated by continuous domestic needs. I hoped that what was lost in the fragmentation would be made up for by originality. She talked to Lili while Emily and I did the last respiratory patterning with Doran. By 10.30 p.m. the boy was asleep.

Alison came over. 'Lili's very intelligent, isn't she?'

'Lili's an artist. Congratulations on recognizing the fact,' I laughed.

In the course of the conversation I discovered that Alison had no idea I was vegetarian; besides this she was ravenously hungry. In an effort to convert her I threw in every herb on the shelf. The result looked superb.

Alison took a mouthful, chewed it, and grimaced appreciatively.

'Do you like it?' said Emily. 'The food here is the *best*.'

'Yes.' Pause. 'It just takes a bit of getting used to.' She chewed on.

When she was three quarters of the way through, I was tempted to taste the stuff myself. It was unpalatably bitter.

'I was too enthusiastic with the herbs. Try some bread and cheese.'

Alison ate a sandwich and we talked about where biology ended and physics began; but she went to bed still worried about the food. In the morning she struggled to hold Doran down while she fixed a nappy between his legs. He wriggled just enough in each direction to be without the nappy ten minutes later when his team spilled over the doorstep.

'Has Doran beaten you?' I asked, finishing the job myself and lifting him on to the table. She had equal difficulty with the stretch suits which Doran wore; they had their feet cut out so that Doran could wear them like long johns.

'Alison, you have Doran's foot in the arm hole,' I said, 'and the suit goes underneath his trousers not on top.'

On Valentine's Day Emily left. As a wild gesture she had starved herself for three days before her departure and then bought a vast piece of chocolate confectionery to share as her parting gift.

The weekend afterwards, Magda came down to find Doran creeping in the garden wearing a red plastic suit and his cosmic anti-sit device which glinted dramatically in the sunshine. Alison had decided to make an expedition along the bank of the stream with a packet of cheese sandwiches for company. She came back early.

'It's your day off,' I said.

'I know, but if I'm going to help Doran I can't think like that. I'd rather work with you.'

'Like friends, you mean?' I said.

'That's right,' she smiled.

'It's a pity Alison hasn't seen Doran crawling,' Magda said, 'because even I didn't believe he really would creep.'

'*You* didn't! Oh Magda, I never guessed.'

'I've known too many children like Doran. I couldn't believe it. I wish an English doctor could have recorded the change in him over the past six months.'

At this point my next door neighbour, an elderly gardener who looked like an historic part of Sussex leaned over the fence, 'What's he got that thing on his back for?'

I told him. George grumbled, 'That'll do 'im no good. I never saw a child like 'im recover.'

'Well you're seeing it now,' Magda replied pleasantly.

'Go on with 'ee,' said George, and turned away to dig his potato patch.

When Alison and I tidied up that night I asked, 'What do you make of it? Be honest.'

'I can see you think you're getting results and that's what counts for me.'

'Alison, making Doran well is going to change the lives of other brain injured children. Do you need the dustpan?'

She took a step towards the cupboard and hesitated. 'I'm a person who wants to concentrate all her energy into one thing. It's useless my thinking about the other children. I want to win for Doran.'

'That's okay because whatever you do for him can't help but have an influence on other people. In the end, whether you want it or not, everybody wins.'

Alison took out the dustpan.

'I really like it here. The funny thing is I told CSV I'd take anything so long as it had nothing to do with children or the mentally handicapped.'

'That's hilarious. Why did you come?'

'I also told them I wanted to go somewhere I could discuss things, and they recommended you.'

'You have to be quick or clever to squeeze the words in round the programme. The alternative is to stay up all night.' The conversation went on past midnight. Doran was restlessly looking for his first drink when we went upstairs. Alison said, 'I shall be worried now if you're tired.'

'You've not deprived me,' I laughed. 'Doran is much worse; he can't stay asleep.'

'What's the matter with him?'

'Basically just being brain injured. He breathes badly, with his mouth open so he's thirsty; and he's not supple enough to get comfortable. If he tries to scratch his nose in the night it's more likely he'll give himself a thump in the eye.'

'Will it change?'

I yawned, stretched and gave her a hug. 'You are changing it by doing the programme.'

The next day Alison was up early. I heard her sliding downstairs in her clogs. She began to clear the house out and invent some kind of foolproof system for the arrangement of cards. Emily had originated a highly effective method of her own which was too esoteric to be passed on. Lili helped by putting all that was designated rubbish into a large black plastic bag.

Diana came in the afternoon bringing another kind of tea, without caffeine.

'You're lucky with your new helper,' she said. 'You should feel a lot better now.'

'I do, except for this small amount of indigestion.'

By the end of the afternoon the indigestion was worse. Diana recommended camomile which we still kept in large quantities, but later in the evening nothing could prevent me doubling up.

'Sorry, Alison, I had an ulcer,' I said. 'The scar tissue is rather over sensitive to stress. I thought I could joke it off.'

The most comfortable position seemed to be on my hands and knees but even that didn't last long.

Alison brought medicine from my doctor and nursed me through the night. Her organization prevailed. She fed me poached egg for the rest of the week and instructed me to wear a hot water bottle. By the time I was well she was expert in putting on nappies fast and appeared to have spent the greater part of her life working with children, particularly brain injured small boys on neurological programmes. Apart from leaving Lili at play school, when it was in fact half term, her results were totally therapeutic.

The next time Magda came, Alison went home for a day. When she arrived back I asked her if she'd enjoyed the peace.

'No,' she said, 'I couldn't take it; I was leaping up out of my chair all the time waiting for bells to go off. On top of that my mother thought I must be vegetarian by now and made me a salad.'

'Did you eat it?'

'No! I rushed to the fridge, dug out every piece of meat I could find and fried it up with two eggs and a plate of chips.'

Perhaps the change of diet affected Alison's digestion – or perhaps it was the sound of bells in her head that prevented her from sleeping – but that night, I was awakened by a figure near my bed.

'I can smell smoke. The house is on fire.'

The children lay serenely asleep but fumes were already drifting into the room. I shut the door behind me, there was no alternative but to walk boldly downstairs. All I knew about how to deal with fires came out of children's books. I wondered whether I'd be better at throwing Doran and Lili out of the bedroom window or catching them in the garden. The wallpaper by the fireplace was smouldering and I saw that an ember must have fallen into an asbestos fire glove which was burning slowly by the skirting board. We poured water until all hissing ceased and then opened windows and doors to let the smoke disperse into night air.

The Institutes had a great saying: 'If your house burns down go to your neighbour and carry on patterning. Let the firemen take care of the fire.' Our neighbours never knew what they had been spared.

Next morning the house was a little chilly, but otherwise substantial. Doran had stopped doing bunny hops and begun creeping well in the garden. He didn't mind getting his hands muddy; he was glad to be so free. I could hear Alison saying, 'Up, up, up Doran. That's excellent' – as he crept towards the apple tree.

'Alison you sound so impeccably English.'

That night Alison read the bedtime story on the sofa with Lili and Doran on either side. Doran watched Alison cross her legs and then lay back and carefully crossed his own.

'He must admire you,' I said. 'You saved our lives last night.'

'I don't understand why I woke up. I had a compulsion to go and check everything.'

'We have a history of disasters or near disasters depending on how you look at the outcome.'

'I'm sure nothing really bad is going to happen to you while I'm here.'

'That's a very unscientific remark, but coming from you, Alison, I'm prepared to believe it.'

12

LIFE CLOSE TO THE EDGE suited Alison; she delivered cups of tea with the spirit of the blitz. My drink was usually lost as I pursued Doran from room to room. Alison cornered me, 'Linda, attend to your own fluid balance and respect the effort I have made to make you this tenth cup.'

While we were out creeping she cleaned the living room and put music on the stereo. So ended my self-imposed exile from the world of Beethoven, Mahler and David Bowie. The first time Alison came out with us, Doran surpassed himself by creeping two hundred and fifty yards non-stop round the vicarage. We were down with him most of the way; so were three dogs and the vicar.

Close to our departure, Bert appeared with the tickets and currency. 'See that she doesn't lose either of them,' she warned Alison.

Hilary brought a bunch of coat hangers supporting my clean laundry and stood over me while I put it in my case.

On the morning of the flight we were immaculately prepared. Alison was drinking red wine, holding the tickets and affecting the laid back calm of a bored pop star, although she kept asking me, 'Linda, aren't you excited yet?'

Since Doran was now a creeper he could do his floor programme on the aircraft. In the departure lounge he attempted an experimental climb up the emergency wheelchair and collected a large bump, but the disfigurement didn't dampen his spirits. We landed smoothly. Hilary was reintroduced to Judith, and two days later we were back on the crowded floor of the Clinic. Doran's creeping caused immediate excitement.

Rising to his audience, he pulled himself up and stood by the chairs; then, full of bravado, he began sliding his hands along them for support and walking round the room. Rosalind arrived to watch him.

'I came to congratulate Doran on his creeping, but the kid's now a cruiser.'

'After such a quick change from a plant to a ship, I expect him to fly himself home.'

'Mrs Scotson, I'm sure he could do it!'

Cataloguing Doran's achievement gave everyone pleasure. He was growing at ninety-one percent of average, which was a hundred and twenty-four percent better than before the programme. Changes in his height and head size were excellent. His chest had grown 3.1 cm which was 1.1 above the average increase.

'We have a word reserved for this sort of thing,' Rosalind remarked. 'Write down "fantastic".'

By the time we came to review the intelligence programme there were few superlatives left. After about five minutes Rosalind stopped us and said, 'Wait a minute, do you realize something?'

We looked blank.

'I'll tell you. You kids have done two and a half times more of the intelligence than I scheduled you.'

After another pause we all doubled up laughing.

'I gave you a pretty stiff job anyway,' Rosalind went on. 'I've heard of parents not managing to complete all their programme, but never in the history of the Institutes to do more than double it.'

Judith closed her eyes. 'I've been going to sleep for months with breeds of dogs marching past my bed.'

'And beetles Judith,' I whispered. 'Don't forget the beetles.'

Doran was unequivocally a star. Hilary said, 'Now that they know you can do anything they'll probably suggest you have him walking the overhead ladder.'

The overhead ladder was to be as high as Doran could comfortably reach with his arms above his head. His bones would then have the correct alignment, making gravity his friend, straightening his body instead of deforming him as it pulled him to the floor. From July he would have the chance to walk independently. His goal was to take five unaided steps.

The only aspect of Doran that had not improved significantly was his speech. We thought this was due to him throwing so much energy into his creeping. Most mid-brain children had auditory problems but it didn't seem to be a prominent factor in Doran's case. Our minds were taken up with the vision of those five steps.

We left Judith in America, and brought back the good news, plus a T shirt with 'I'm gonna win' printed on it, for Alison. As she opened the front door fresh air mingled with the odour of polish and soap powder

'Almost everything's been through the wash, I did think twice when I got to the teddy bears.'

By the time my mother brought Lili back we had begun the new routine. It involved Doran creeping eight hundred yards daily to build up to the mile on his marathon day. The length from the front gate through the house to the end of my very long narrow garden was almost exactly a hundred yards. This meant that somehow or other Doran would have to creep from end to end of it eight times a day, every day, regardless of storm or earthquake. Since we still had to fit in the patterning, respiratory patterning, masking and intelligence, my son would need to show a high level of cooperation.

'Did the Institutes mention how you'd actually get him to do it?' Alison asked.

'They did. It's called the "civil code" programme. We post up a set of rules for the house, and responsibilities for Doran and Lili. They earn chips – I mean plastic tokens, not fried potatoes – for doing well, and with these chips they buy privileges. I've drafted out a sample. Have a look.'

Alison was sceptical.

'Come on,' I said. 'They love games and this is a game they

can win all the time. That's right up your street.'

We bought them both purses and hundreds of large brightly coloured plastic chips. They were impressed. The initial idea was that they should save up throughout the day and buy a privilege before they went to bed.

Waiting all day became a little excessive for Doran, so we invented short term choices for him and wrote them down on a blackboard. A favourite entertainment, such as wheeling him in the wheelbarrow four times round the apple tree, or swinging him by the hands and feet, was more exhausting than doing the programme. The new anti-sit, mark IV, was a success for Doran, although not so comfortable for others. It consisted of an aluminium bar ending in a tail. There were little bolts along the bar which contrived to dig firmly into the stomachs of anyone picking him up.

Doran's speed, and his ability to climb, brought him more knocks and bruises. People worried about them; someone brought him a small crash helmet but it persistently slipped over his eyes and after the first few moments of trying out the new toy, he flatly refused to have anything on his head.

One morning there was a moderate swelling over his temple, by lunch time it had grown into a bump, and over the next few days it appeared to have increased rather than diminished in size. I took him to the doctor.

'It's a small haematoma,' he said. 'He's ruptured a little blood vessel. Don't worry, it should go down.'

The bump began to spread upwards and outwards until one side of Doran's face and head was inflated like a misshapened football. I took him back to the surgery. The news was disconcerting. If the haematoma, which was now one of the worst my GP had ever seen, didn't deflate itself soon, it would have to be drained.

'Does that mean you just syringe out the fluid?' I asked.

'I'm sorry, it's too dangerous a job on the head. Doran would have to go to hospital.'

'For the day?'

'For a few days I'm afraid. It means a general anaesthetic.'

'But that might affect his breathing and cause further brain injury. Couldn't he have a local? I'd be able to hold him.'

'Let's give it a couple more days. In the meantime try to keep him quiet.'

Despite my anxiety I laughed. 'You should try it,' I said.

At the beginning of the trouble Alison had affectionately tried to persuade me that the swelling had decreased, while it was really becoming larger and more even in its distribution. Now she gave up, saying, 'Scientists can't be as objective as mothers.'

'That's because scientists are also human beings and motherhood isn't prohibitive. It admits more abilities than it omits.'

'Only you could say that.'

I phoned the Institutes to leave a message for the doctor in the hope that she would back me on the use of local anaesthetic. I was even more anxious that Doran cease to be so literally swollen headed. 'Maybe if you stop being vain your bump will go down,' I said as I poured witch hazel, my mother's remedy, and arnica, which was anthroposophical, and well recommended by Kirsteen, over him. It trickled through his hair and ran down his neck. The more Doran felt we wanted him to keep still, the more desperate he became to move. We increased his respiratory patterning and cut out some of his creeping, but the result was that he had still more surplus energy. Besides this, the haematoma unbalanced him so that he narrowly escaped colliding with an abundance of chair legs and sharp corners I hadn't noticed before. I stayed up half the night simply looking at his bump as though I could shrink the thing with the force of my eyes. Alison came and found me.

'I couldn't sleep. Would you like a cup of tea?' she asked.

'Please, you're an absolute saint.'

When she came back I said, 'I'm sure it's going down, can you see?'

'We've already established I'm the wrong person to ask.'

I put out my hand and touched Doran's temple, the bone hard surface of the deformation had softened, I could push my fingers into it.

193

'Feel, the fluid's draining away.'

Next morning Doran was appreciably less of a highbrow.

'We won,' I said. 'Crisis over.'

The phone rang over lunch.

'Mrs Scotson, this is the Institutes for the Achievement of Human Potential. I have Dr Wilkinson on the line now.'

'Oh but I don't need her any more. Could you give me Rosalind Klein?'

'Dr Wilkinson wants to talk to you. I'll put you through.'

Dr Wilkinson sounded very calm and supportive. This changed into warm congratulations when she heard my news. Rosalind's manner was less restrained.

'Mrs Scotson, that's great. I'm so relieved. It would be really bad for a child with breathing problems like Doran's to be given a general anaesthetic, and he's doing so well on the programme now. . . .'

We returned to practical problems. Doran needed to 'cruise' between large boxes.

Bert had persuaded her uncle, appropriately named 'Friend', who ran a removal business, to offer us some tea chests. They were fine outside but left very little room for movement in the house and were a great inconvenience for everybody except the children, who were all anxious to stand on top of them.

After a few warm days I decided it would be a treat for Doran to creep on the forest, so we prearranged a marathon day and set out with a picnic. Lili had a pushchair full of bears, and a bucket and spade because some parts of the chosen path were rather sandy. The sky appeared to be bright and sunny; I had an image of Doran leaping out of the car and dashing away into the heather like a small dog. When we arrived, the location was rather more exposed than I'd remembered and Doran showed no inclination whatsoever to claim his freedom. In fact he resented the whole idea; the only direction in which he would rush was back to the car and if that was blocked, he collapsed with his head buried in his arm. We carried him out of sight of our transport, then Alison and Lili went ahead invitingly with the pushchair, the bears and the picnic. Doran's incredulity that we could have expected him to creep in such a godforsaken place increased. The thin wind grew more penetrating, blowing a few little rain clouds over us. Lili protested that it was cold and climbed into the pushchair, insulating herself with teddies. We finally ate our picnic huddled together under a small copse of trees while the rain poured down.

'I still think it was a good idea,' Alison said. 'You had to try it; it just didn't work that's all.'

'There speaks the compassionate voice of science,' I said. 'Have another soggy sandwich.'

The next marathon day was conducted in the lofts and attics of a warm dry house. Doran even crept well, clockwise and anti-clockwise round a settee in the front room of a small council house, providing there were noisy children to chase him. We were ahead of schedule. One morning he had done so well at Hilary's it was worth going for the mile. We drove to the house with lofts and attics which belonged to our friend Sheila. When we came downstairs we saw a Wendy house in Sheila's garden and further on an enclosure with some chickens.

We tried the chickens first, but Doran made it quite clear that what he wanted was the Wendy house. Lili had already taken possession and was laying the table for a dolls' tea party. Sheila gave her a plate of delicately sliced fruit and cheese and a bottle of apple juice. I wriggled in to join her. When Doran reached us we sat him on a chair and offered him a swift stab at afternoon tea. Despite the pressure, Lili always managed to be gracious. Alison paced out the metres, retrieved Doran, and positioned him at different starting points so that the track to the Wendy house would retain some freshness. I peered through the low windows. If anything Doran was going faster. He ate another tea.

'How are you winding him up, Alison?' I asked.

'You and Lili are the key,' she said, retrieving him and taking him back. 'I seem to be the spring.'

An hour and several plates of food later he had beaten paths to us from every direction but was gaining the mood of an Olympic Champion; so was Alison.

'This is it,' she called. 'One more lap Doran and you've done the mile.'

As Doran arrived in triumph Lili and I fell out of the Wendy house to congratulate him.

'Let's carry them both like heroes,' said Alison, lifting Doran on to her shoulders. I bent down so that Lili could climb onto mine.

'You are all three heroes everyday,' I said, 'but just now it really shows. Once more you've made the impossible old hat.'

'I like old hats,' said Lili from above my head.

Peter had built the overhead ladders, and the next day he fitted them to the wall. It was difficult to measure Doran's stretch; the differences between having him holding on easily but with his limbs bent, or looking perfectly straight but too high to grip comfortably, were extremely slight.

My parents had paid for an extension to the kitchen and that was now full of ladders. We had to climb under them to get out of the back door.

'Anyone breaking in here in the night would get a shock,' Peter said. 'He'd be falling over packing cases and banging into ladders. I should think he'd be happy to go to the police station.'

'Peter, I expect all burglars to leave donations. Will you put a collection box on the door to save them possible injury?'

We began our first marathon day on the ladder. Alison and I were naïvely happy; Doran's greatest wish, or so we thought, must be to walk. We had forgotten that he was now an adept creeper, and having consolidated his freedom, being trapped under a ladder was far from his mind. He flatly refused to move. We took it in turns to hold his hands round the rungs while Lili played with various desirable toys ahead of him. Unfortunately this increased his inclination to get down on his hands and knees to reach them. Eventually he stopped grumbling and began screaming; his wrath rose through the window and travelled out across the fields. In a more urban environment the street would have already called out the NSPCC to see how many children we were beating to death. It was the most extreme battle of wills I had ever had with Doran; there could be no question who was going to win, the question was, how?

'Alison,' I shouted over the tumult, 'we'll have to use one hundred percent civil code.'

'Anything to get us out of this.'

So Lili walked the ladder in front of Doran, slowly, in a perfect cross-pattern. Each time she reached the end she earned a chip; every five chips she bought a privilege. She had a day of glory and reward; Doran had the choice of either walking the ladder to achieve the same benefits or lying ignominiously under it, bawling his head off.

'The only step he takes away from that corner,' I vowed, 'will be walking.'

Finally we noticed Doran's howls decrease; he had gone to sleep. I tucked a rug round him and left him while we ate lunch; I comforted myself that at least Lili was having a superb time. When Doran woke I fed him on the floor; above him loomed the inescapable destiny of a line of rungs.

Just before tea time, as Lili collected her last chip, Doran changed his mind. He clamped his hands down and began walking after her.

'He's seen the light. Hallelujah!'

I rushed to the fruit bowl to seize a banana, he received his chip and quickly bought a large piece.

Gradually we built up the number of trips per privilege. Then to gain more time we tried letting him buy the privilege of having a book read to him while he walked. Nevertheless the programme now took up to 11.30 p.m. to complete. It often ended with a half hour respiratory patterning during which Doran fell asleep on the table. When we'd finished I was very tempted to put my head down beside his and sleep too. More than once I was woken gently by Alison.

'You've been there twenty minutes, I was afraid you were going to fall off.'

'I go on doing this in my dreams,' I said. 'Sometimes we seem like the mechanical figures on top of a famous clock.'

From time to time we took turns clearing up or reading aloud. Alison had the *New Scientist* every week and found a piece of research that she thought I'd enjoy, either because I was sympathetic or because it would stimulate an argument. I answered her with a mixture of philosophy, spiritual science and art. Alison's intellectual honesty made me more secure, but I still had to face criticism. One of my friends who had moved to Forest Row to be close to the Steiner School, suggested that I was in danger of hardening Doran's spiritual nature by giving him pictures of things he'd not encountered in his every day experience.

'But a child invents things all the time,' I said, a little bemused. 'What about fairies and giants?'

'They are imaginary in the first place. I won't read my son stories about lions and tigers because he hasn't been to the zoo yet.'

'But I don't like zoos, and where else does Doran go to see wild animals? Must I wait until we can go to India before I read him the *Just So Stories*?'

The argument went unresolved since neither of us could resurrect Dr Steiner to have his opinion. Nevertheless I was saddened by her. Doran himself seemed unusually attuned to people's feelings and often anticipated our thoughts.

Despite our civil code victory and the fact that Doran was now walking under his ladder, I wasn't happy with its height. Doran's arms were a little bent and his spine didn't look straight enough, I doubted that he was getting the right information. Nevertheless many people who came thought it already put a strain on his heart to reach up as high as he did. When I could bear things no longer I telephoned Peter to ask if he would raise the ladder. He was out. I sat down in the kitchen and put my head in my hands.

'Alison, I'm so weak. It's terrible I let myself be hurt over silly things. That ladder is ruining Doran and I haven't faced it because I can't bear any more disapproval.'

'You're not weak, your patterners believe in you, they come because you need them and they admire what you're doing for Doran.'

'The problem is I want to be open to so many people and I suppose I keep hoping they understand me.'

'That's asking a bit much, Linda. You're the most unusual person I've ever met.'

'Am I? I thought you were!'

'I wasn't aware I was unusual until I came here. I'm beginning to see myself differently now. Can we get someone else to put the ladders up? I can't bear you to say you're weak; it's not you.'

I laughed at her. 'You're right, somehow I can always stand up when I need to.'

We examined the ladders and found that the ends could be lifted a little by the addition of a few books. Doran was now straight and very willing to stand under the rungs with his arms above his head; but he would not or could not walk.

'So we'll pattern him on the ladder,' I said. 'We can move his arms and legs ourselves.'

'That means one of us shuffles around on her knees holding on to his feet while the other does his hands.'

'I'm afraid so. Have you got tough knees?'

'After years of being kicked on the hockey field, I'd say I could manage.'

We tried, until Alison said, 'I think I can do both. You and Lili concentrate on motivation.' Doran reacted like a theatrical producer giving auditions. Some things were worth chips and others weren't. He had a box full of scarves and hats so I put a mirror at one end so that he could chose his head gear and walk down the ladder to admire himself. By evening he was going well for 'candle lit suppers' which involved toasting small pieces of cheese over a candle stuck into a Mateus Rosé bottle. We didn't speculate whether or not smoked cheese was good for him.

Peter must have been on holiday and remained inaccessible. When Diana came on Monday, she saw the books and immediately contacted a carpenter called James who lived in the village but hadn't got a car. If someone was prepared to collect him he could come over the following evening; the books would last until then.

Doran kept on walking. To approach his daily goal there was no question of stopping until he felt tired; Lili preferred to stay with us and go to sleep on an improvised bed of flowered eiderdowns beside the ladders. We often worked until midnight with Alison's clock radio for company.

'Did you know about the SAS,' she said. 'To qualify, a soldier has to go through an incredibly tough course. When he finally drags himself in to what he thinks is base he's told he has to do another ten miles. Few can take it.'

'Soldiers aren't that tough. Did you know the American army tried to compete with a group of two-year-olds energywise for a day, and they failed.'

'I wouldn't. I'm SAS material – if only they accepted women!'

'Alison, underneath all this military show I'm sure you're a pacifist at heart.'

'I've too much energy. I need things to be intense.'

'I see, you're a kind of nineteenth century throw back, with strange inconsistencies. Your heroes are the Sex Pistols and the Queen.'

'They're both brilliant.'

'In their own line, you're right. Was Doran yawning or laughing?'

'Yawning.'

'He can go to bed. I'll stay here on my knees ready for tomorrow; it's less painful than getting up.'

'Do you pray on your knees?'

'No, in my opinion prayer is action . . . Okay Alison, pull me to my feet.'

She put out her hand.

We concluded that if James came between five and six p.m. he'd have done the work while Doran was having his patterning —respiratory patterning and the last of his creeping. (He was still scheduled to creep eight hundred metres a day.)

While Alison was out shopping one of the evening team rang to report that her car had broken down and she needed a lift. So, by the time Alison arrived back there was no alternative for her but to drive off in the opposite direction. She'd just got through the door again when James telephoned to say he was ready to be picked up.

'Remember the SAS, Alison,' I remarked comfortingly as we arranged Doran on the table and started to sing. Twenty minutes later she had delivered James with a large bag of tools and was reaching for the bread knife.

'I'm starving. I've had a large piece of toast and marmite floating in front of me all the way home.'

She put on the grill. James unzipped his bag and announced, 'I've forgotten my saw.'

It was a particular type of saw which he could not do without.

Alison turned off the grill and escorted James back to the car.

'In the SAS,' she said, 'perhaps I forgot to tell you, the soldiers who go on to the next ten miles find out it's a hoax. They're actually given hot tea with buns a quarter of a mile down the road.'

'We pacifists are much more ruthless, Alison. Buy a bottle of cider on me and tomorrow I'll write to the War Office to recommend you.'

As the weather grew warmer we could do the ladder work with the door and windows open. Doran started his day at nine a.m., when he had a half hour respiratory session. Someone came in especially for that period so that Lili had Alison's company for breakfast. If we didn't finish till midnight the chances were I wouldn't anticipate my first sleep until well after one, which meant I rose in a kind of dream. It seemed to be nature's way of reducing the strain. I owned a black dressing gown which had a certain style about it, and if I put on my shoes there seemed to be very little necessity for me to dress, still less reason to brush my hair; I simply flowed from the night into the day programme. My health visitor could never quite make up her mind whether I was getting up or going to bed.

By lunch time Doran was negotiating his ritual course in the garden. He had an infuriating way of picking a daisy to offer with the kind of smile that indicated how much nicer it would be to sit still and make daisy chains. One afternoon when Alison and Lili were out he refused to do anything except pull me on to the warm grass, laughing and handing out flowers. I taxed him chip after chip. I spoke firmly and pushed him.

He resisted anger. The sky was a luminous blue and the birds were singing; there was nothing I would have liked better than to have agreed with him. This made matters considerably worse. Half an hour later when Alison arrived back, we were still only a few yards away from the top of the garden. Doran remained serene while I shouted at him. Then his first helper arrived. She stood on her head by the apple tree. The effect was magic. He moved rapidly in her direction. I shook my fist at him.

'I've never seen you angry before,' Alison said, 'it's quite frightening.'

'Doran doesn't seem to think so. There must be an easier way of motivating him before I tear him limb from limb.'

'What about the civil code?'

'Doran appears to have cracked it. Everything has limits. We need a revised system for creeping.'

Doran was continuing to creep towards his friend who inverted herself intermittently in front of him.

'I think I'll try a hypnotist,' I said with sudden resolution.

'That's a bit far out. Where would you find one?'

'Round here it's easy. I'll look in the yellow pages.'

The next marathon creeping day I left Doran to have his lunch and went off to the nearest hypnotist. I hadn't the slightest idea what to expect, but if people could give up smoking or have babies under hypnosis, doubtless they could crawl. The hypnotist in question was very kind; he pointed out·that in the case of young children one didn't use hypnotism but suggestion. Then he taught me a way of deepening Doran's sleep so that he would be receptive. We discussed the games he'd most like to play while he was creeping. I was to sit by his head at night and whisper, 'Doran, you're a train that never stops, a train that never stops, a train that never stops' – and then remind him of this while he was creeping.

I rushed out to the car and drove back to Alison repeating all the phrases he'd told me. By the time I arrived I was in danger of believing I was an inter-continental express and crashing through the front room.

'What are you muttering?' Alison asked.

'I'm a train that never stops – never stops. . . .'

That night and for the ensuing nights, I tried the phrases out. Over the next few days we crawled beside Doran chanting the relevant lines; but it was impossible to tell whether it was the suggestion or our behaviour he found the greater motivation.

The weather changed. It rained steadily, Lili and Alison went to the Summer Fayre at Emerson College. They watched maypole dancing through humid windows and ate strawberry gateau with heaps of ice cream. Doran was happy because Magda had come down for the day, he suddenly shook off my hands and began to walk down the ladder towards her.

'Magda, how did you do it?'

'Isn't that what he normally does?' she asked.

When Alison and Lili came back with a small bag of wholemeal biscuits, which looked as if they had nothing undesirable in them, Doran wandered nonchalantly along to accept one. Lili wanted to feed him.

'If you give me two chips you can take over his privilege,' I said. Lili put her hand in her chip purse; what chips she had were sandwiched between a gunge of half-melted chocolate. She withdrew her hand and licked her fingers.

'I didn't see a thing,' I said.

While Magda stayed, Doran walked; when she left he developed some mysterious problems in his hands and feet and by evening we were back on our hands and knees.

'He can do it,' I said. 'So he should do it.'

Alison had an inspiration. 'Wouldn't it be good if we made a tunnel out of hardboard. We could hang strange things at one end, he'd have to walk through it to get at them. He wouldn't want to stand around in the dark.'

Her plan was to enclose the whole ladder but we compromised and brought James along to cover half of it. Doran immediately disappeared inside the tunnel and stayed put.

Neither of us was small enough to squeeze in and get him out; he hummed to himself and banged on the hardboard for amusement. We left him; it was a war of attrition. When we came back Doran had made an exit and could be found in the 'God-awful', quietly playing with Lili's lego.

'When the weather gets better we can try a ladder in the garden, Alison. Not that it solves our present problem.'

I grabbed Doran, shook him, and fixed him back on the rungs. Alison said, 'I have a great idea, let's rip the tunnel off.'

'It may still work. Couldn't we find a way to push him through?'

We widened the tunnel by undoing the board at the bottom so that it opened like a tent. This meant that one of us could slide in and chase Doran out of it. There was a lot of unfair fighting, in these restricted surroundings Doran was more agile than either of us.

An uninformed spectator would have felt unnerved by the sight of the hardboard bouncing frantically, but Doran was finally disgorged, walking.

I decided to recommence brushing my hair in honour of the approach of July; it took two hours to get the tangle out of it. When I emerged from the bathroom it was nearly half past one in the morning.

Alison was reading *The Selfish Gene* by Richard Dawkins. 'You should look after yourself from now on,' she said.

'At the moment my heart comes before my appearance.'

Alison put down her book. 'This chap reckons all so-called generous impulses are to preserve the genes. The genes use us to march on; we are simply gene machines.'

'Poor devil,' I said, 'if he wants to prove that, it's his folly.

Beyond the gene is the election and beyond that ultimately, the transcendent power of the human spirit.'

'Anyway your hair looks better now and I believe it was your genes that drove you to brush it.'

She handed me Doran's bottle and we went upstairs. The next day by a merciful intercession a home help arrived. Her name was Julie and the first door she tried was George's. She didn't stay and he must have been disappointed because Julie's visits were in their own way miracles; she became a wonderful friend.

Peter came back from his holiday and built a ladder along by the fence. Although the sky was overcast it was warm and worth working outside. George came out from his greenhouse to give Doran some strawberries.

''E'll never walk, you'll have his arms out of their sockets first.'

Doran progressed cheerfully towards a hose-pipe spouting water into a pyramid of buckets and bowls. July was the month to begin encouraging him to make his first independent lunges between two seated people. When he crossed this abyss successfully he won a piece of banana; so banana became an elevated and exotic fruit only obtainable through the highest effort.

Having salvaged my own appearance, I turned to Lili's. Her curls entwined themselves in familiar knots. Cathy had held her down and patiently brushed but it had not been in Emily's nature to perpetuate any time-consuming grooming; as a result Lili's hair had woven itself into several layers of matted blanket. Alison decided to put the whole matter into the hands of a hairdresser. I was sitting watching Doran doing some courageous lunges, when the couple returned. Lili sat on Alison's back, looking like a shorn elf; Alison was white and shaking.

'Did you keep her hair?' I asked.

'No I didn't. I was very glad to leave it behind. You should have been there. She was rolling about on the floor screaming; they had to follow her around on hands and knees.'

'They made an awfully good job of it.'

'The manager felt sure Lili would hate hairdressers for the

rest of her life, but as soon as it was over she stood up and thanked everybody. Anyway, how's Doran?'

Alison's complexion remained pale. In the middle of lunch she suddenly sprang up and began searching in the drawer of the dresser. She produced a torch, went over to the mirror, opened her mouth and peered intently down her throat.

'What exactly are you doing?' I asked.

'Looking at my tonsils.'

'What on earth for?'

'Signs of stress. I have chronic tonsillitis. There it is, the little white blobs, you see?'

I couldn't. She took a spoon handle and pointed them out. She continued to monitor her condition daily with the torch; I got used to seeing her with her mouth open.

'It would be useful if you could read the future in there too,' I said. 'We need Doran to make a breakthrough – and a windfall for the Fund.'

Bert called in the evening. She had her 'office' and a pair of dungarees for Doran. The knees of his trousers continuously disintegrated with the force of his creeping and neither Alison nor I were good at putting on patches. Bert wanted to wait until he'd earned a privilege before handing over the package. In the meantime there was this year's sponsored crawl to be considered.

'We need a lot of sponsorship. Diana can't do it because she has trouble with her heart. Your getting back to the Institutes depends upon us being really well organized.'

'Put me down,' said Alison, 'I'm going to win!'

'It's not a race, love,' said Bert.

'I'll do better if I see it like that; you should be pleased. If I put all my energy into it, the result will be good for Doran.'

Doran was hanging from his ladder; he caught sight of the package and pointed animatedly, 'Cor, cor.'

'No, Doran it's not a car,' said Bert. 'Let's see what you can do first.'

He fell off and crept over to her. We positioned ourselves appropriately for lunging. Doran's eyes were riveted to his parcel. He took one completely independent step and swept it off Bert's knee. She loosened the string and gave it to him to unwrap.

'He did that for you, Bert,' I said, as she helped him proudly into the trouser legs. 'What's the date?'

We looked at the calendar. It was the fourth of July. Bert whistled, 'I have to hand it to you, Doran; you chose quite a memorable day to celebrate INDEPENDENCE!'

13

---*---

We were planning publicity for the crawl; Hilary offered the number of a Fleet Street journalist who arrived with his photographer.

A long article entitled 'Love that Worked a Miracle' appeared on page three of the *Sunday People*. Doran became overnight news, only displaced from the front page by the Brixton riots. Phone calls from desperate parents poured in.

A woman living in South London wanted to come down and see us. Since Mina didn't mention a husband, I put her quickly into the category of determined single parents, hard pushed to find money. I was willing to send her the train fare but she said she could get a lift.

The Crowborough National Childbirth Trust were patterning Doran. While I was explaining whom they should expect someone said, 'Does your working class, single parent mum own a chauffeur-driven Mercedes, because one's just pulled up at the gate?'

We all rushed to the window to watch the chauffeur help Mina, her children and her nannie out of the car. She produced a Harrods bag with clothes for Doran plus a two foot long cake weighted by fresh cream and half peaches. Mina understood the meaning of intensity; this seemed to be a decisive factor. People who came in search of help for their children often felt that every waking minute should be spent doing something; they were relieved to see this really happening. If not, they were usually very shaken within the first five minutes of their arrival.

When Mina had watched Doran being patterned we swung

him down and lifted her son up. Doran crept over and tugged at my legs. Since I didn't stop, he buried his face melodramatically in the carpet. 'I had no idea you were so possessive,' I cried.

He had deeper feelings on the matter than any of us could have imagined, so Alison diplomatically removed him to the garden.

Mina intended to go to the Institutes. As we said goodbye she remarked, 'I read that you have a fund for Doran. Let me give you a little towards it.'

She folded the cheque. I didn't open it until the white Mercedes had disappeared down the lane, then I saw that Mina had donated us £100.

The article went on getting results. I was plunged into correspondence either thanking people who had sent money or telling people about Doran's treatment. At first I insisted on being very detailed, every letter reminded me of my own desperation and the joy which followed. One evening when I was just finishing my tenth page to a woman in Ireland, Alison intervened.

'It's one thirty in the morning; you'll be dead if you go on like this.'

'Do you think I'm crazy to want to give people so much happiness?'

'No, but you could simply provide them with the names of the book and the place to go. What about photocopying a letter?'

'It's too near the heart. Would you like a photocopied letter?'

'If I was that desperate I wouldn't care. Suppose you get ill?'

'This is the last one, Alison.'

'Until tomorrow,' she said. 'How can I look after you when you're so stubborn.'

'Would I be doing this programme if I were sensible.'

'Probably you wouldn't, but do try to show a little good sense. Here I've stamped you an envelope; put your letter in it and go to bed.'

The following week Alison and Lili went round the local industrial estate with a sheaf of sponsorship forms.

'The manager of "Tantofex" promised he'd have everyone in the factory sponsor Doran before he'd hand out their pay packets!' Alison exclaimed. She had £200 on her back, which of course was going to be heavily supported by her knees.

Besides Alison's sponsors, some firms decided to send their own candidates. Crawling caught the imagination; employees made trial circuits of the typing pool or the factory floor. We had the same desperation about the weather as we'd done the year before, but the best we could wring out of the Met. Office was 'changeable'. 'King George's field' proved to be the only sunny place for miles around. Doran arrived and began creeping animatedly in all directions to prove that a few roundabouts and sideshows were all that had been lacking from Ashdown Forest. I intended him to join the competitors on the track but I hadn't risked anyone actually sponsoring him.

The creepers, or crawlers, depending on one's definition, set off in a bunch; then they rapidly spread out over the field. The winner would be the one who combined raising the highest sponsorship money with completing all fifteen laps. Doran on his own initiative set out after them. He made a smaller and smaller figure as he reached the far side of the track, weaving between the competitors and finally coming up to the table where Judy Blowe sat to record the laps. Alison was already way ahead; she acknowledged our waving with a salute. She outlapped her colleagues and was easily the first home, which, since it was not a race was more significant to herself than Bert. Nevertheless, she had the most sponsorship money to collect and became the undisputed winner of the champions' shield.

'I spent the last twenty minutes crawling along with the local candidate for the Ecology Party,' she said. 'We were so deep in discussion I had to be stopped from doing an extra lap.'

'You do seem to be drawn to pacifists, Alison. What would you like to celebrate?'

'Fish and chips,' she said.

With the sponsorship money and the money we'd raised

through the *Sunday People*, our flight was no longer at risk. This gave me more time to worry about Doran's programme. As his ladder walks increased it was hard to finish his creeping in the daytime; he needed somewhere exciting to go in the evenings.

Lili's play school and the village school itself, were plausible alternatives. The headmaster of the Primary School had retired and the new headmaster hadn't arrived, so the responsibility for its security lay with the vicar who gladly gave his consent.

We began with the play school. At the sight of the toys Doran thought he'd struck it lucky and had to be firmly relieved of the illusion that he'd come to play. He had just been persuaded to creep three times round the place before expecting to go on the slide, when we were startled by a forceful knocking at the door. I answered it, and was overwhelmed by a small crowd of Italians and a golden retriever dog, which bounded in knocking Doran over, first with its head, and then with its tail. We established that their car had broken down and that they were in search of a telephone or a garage. Since what we were doing was obviously incomprehensible, one half of their party went off to find more realistic help. The other half accepted sips of tea from our Thermos flask and the retriever dog was commandeered as motivation for Doran's creeping.

Although we didn't listen to the BBC or read the papers, news of the Royal Wedding hadn't failed to reach us. People kept asking how we were going to celebrate. 'By a marathon day on the ladders,' I said. But Lili was anxious to know how one became a real princess and whether Doran could be a real prince.

The answer was to have our own wedding. The outdoor ladder became the nave of St Paul's while Doran and Lili dressed up to enact the story as it was reported from Alison's radio.

George came through his lettuce patch. ''Ere,' he said, presenting Lili with a bouquet of green cos. Then he turned to me and went on, 'You shouldn't be working 'im on a day like this, t'aint good for 'im.'

'Actually, we're celebrating.'

'You ought to let 'em watch television.'

'We don't have one.'

'You bring 'em round. They'll be showin' it again tonight.'

So as the crowning privilege we walked the four feet between George's front door and my own, to sit in front of his rather faulty black and white television screen. The curious changes in the dome of St Paul's, through a defect in the horizontal hold, and the fact that Geore couldn't make up his mind whether the wedding was better received on the BBC or ITV, only enhanced the innocent wonder we all took in the small screen.

'Did I really marry Doran?' Lili asked.

'Just for the day, Lili,' I said. 'After midnight he's back to being your brother.'

By the end of July the ladder walking was going well. The damp humid weather seemed ominous, but brought no catastrophies. Doran usually wore nothing but his chip purse and a pair of high topped boots with holes in the toes. After the end of each trip he stamped his foot into the bucket and squelched about like a circus clown.

At night there were thunderstorms. The loudest and most violent brought Alison to my door. 'May I stay for a while?' she asked, 'I keep thinking we're going to be hit.'

Lightning streaked my window and appeared to glance off the mirror. Doran and Lili remained asleep.

A few nights later Alison's sleep was disturbed by a nightingale. Just after midnight, she took me outside to listen. This was the only nightingale either of us had ever heard. We stood deferentially, almost suspended in time.

It had been over a year since Lili came with us to the Institutes. She'd made a considerable impression there and I knew that they stressed the importance of having the whole family together for evaluations. I broached the subject to Bert.

'You can take Lili by all means,' she said, 'but can you cope?'

'It would be superbly helpful to have Alison.'

Bert looked stern, 'That will cost us a lot.'

'We do have the money.'

'It was hard won and we don't want to waste it . . . But on the other hand I do think Lili needs to go with you. Would Alison want to go? It's a pretty exhausting job I should think.'

Alison was more than willing. She had never been in an aeroplane before. 'You'll need something to play with,' Lili told her.

Lili went off early for a holiday with my parents. By way of compensation Abigail and Rebecca Kops, daughters of the friends with whom we'd spent Christmas when Doran was in Guy's hospital, arrived. They threw themselves into water fights which were Doran's favourite summer sport. He raced down his ladder for the pleasure of holding the hose and learnt that if he put his finger over the nozzle he could produce a forceful spray. Doran had the advantage of being nearly naked during these attacks, the rest of us spent most of the day in wet clothes. There was a great retaliation, during which the lawn was flooded before a final armistice; Doran lost all further interest in water. Baths were resisted, even a wash behind the ears appeared a potential assault.

Time was a problem. We had taken to eating picnic teas sitting at each end of the ladder while Doran walked between two plates, chewing as he went. After tea we packed up to go to the local school.

Doran crept through a maze of desks piled with their up-turned chairs, down the narrow corridor lined with books and stuffed animals in glass cases, to the vast shiny expanse of the gym floor. It was a pretty school; I wondered if he would ever become a daytime pupil. He wasn't yet three – he'd already taken a step – but his body looked so fragile; I couldn't predict when his spindly legs would ever take his weight.

In early August a short period of sunshine brought out a

concentration of insects; the air was thick with humming and buzzing. 12 August was my thirty-sixth birthday and my mother was bringing Lili home. I expected Magda, and Bernard and Erica Kops were due to pick up their children. By one o'clock everyone sat in the shade of the apple tree eating lunch.

'You'll write a book about this one day,' Bernard began. 'Where are you going? I just started to talk to you.'

Alison said, 'She's just getting Doran's mask.'

'It's your birthday. Are you enjoying yourself?' Bernard persisted.

'Believe me, I am; it's a great way of life. Some people climb mountains.'

'You mean it's a drug?' he asked.

'No,' said Erica, 'she means she's no alternative.'

When the Kopses had gone, Magda suggested we take the children out for tea at a children's zoo, a short drive away.

'We could do all Doran's creeping,' she said, 'and there are no caged lions; you'll approve of it.'

'Magda we can't; we'll lose time.'

'You can,' Alison said. 'A change of scene would be good for Doran; one can be too obsessional.'

'Can one?'

'I promise you Doran won't miss anything.'

I looked at them. 'Since you're my close friends and it's my birthday, I'm in your hands.'

When we arrived Doran immediately crept past the zoo turnstile and on full steam to the duck pond. Alison caught him by one leg, as he reached towards a feathered tail.

I noticed other visitors thought Doran was creeping for amusement, not because he couldn't walk. He committed the classic error of mistaking a tortoise for a stone. When we paused for tea a band of monkeys descended from the trees, stealing the food out of our fingers. Doran liked feeding animals, and encouraged them.

'You'll have to watch out for this in the tropical rain forest, Alison,' said Magda.

'And how will you survive the storms?' I asked. 'I suppose you're all right with spiders?'

'As long as they're reasonably small,' she said.

The next time we were doing the ladder indoors I found a moderately sized spider and showed it to Doran, who advanced inquisitively along his rungs. So, to encourage him to move faster, I pretended to put the innocent creature down Alison's neck. She screamed and fled while Doran made one of his quickest recorded trips. Alison returned looking sheepish.

'I thought that was within your limits,' I said.

'It must have been a borderline case,' she answered.

Later that week she came home with a huge black rubber spider.

'Perhaps it will help me get used to them?'

We threw the spider happily at each other throughout the day; Doran found the whole game very stimulating. But, after dark, Alison became genuinely afraid of its uncomfortably realistic appearance. Next morning she regained prestige in her own eyes. She found her dissecting tools, dug up a worm and made a perfect dissection for him to watch as he walked.

A short while after this my friend began scrutinizing the post for the results of her grant application. There were two assessments in fairly quick succession. When the letter arrived, her first failure didn't mean she should give up hope, nevertheless the suppressed emotion went straight to her tonsils. The next time she examined them they were festooned with unpleasant white blobs requiring a course of antibiotics. She also developed a high temperature. I put her gently to bed but she preferred to wander about carrying a pile of blankets and alternated between working and falling into them.

That evening the team from Uckfield Lionesses included a hairdresser who had promised to turn Doran into a modern man. While he sat on my knee with a clean tea cloth tucked round his neck, Lili held up a mirror so that he could appreciate the change. Curls fell and a new sleek image emerged. Doran beamed.

'He looks a little like David Bowie,' said Alison. 'Come on Dor, let's dance.'

The next time we turned up at the school, the new headmaster had arrived. He caught us red-handed creeping round his classrooms. I forgot that he and I were about the same age and jumped up like a naughty infant, protesting, 'We did have permission from the vicar.'

He pointed out that the school was now his responsibility. We constituted a security risk and we would have to go.

This was a minor catastrophe; I couldn't immediately think of anywhere else with the advantage of being near and open at night. Alison suggested trying the Old Convent which had been converted into a Barclays Bank Training Centre. The building remained a rambling Gothic affair surrounded by pine forest. Permission was graciously granted, we were offered the east wing and the old chapel for our creeping ground. The chapel was now a huge thickly carpeted lecture theatre, but we could still smell incense, and the setting sun glowed evocatively through the high stained-glass windows.

One evening Doran turned off down the corridor into the depth of the east wing, while Alison ran ahead to turn on lights. The final switch revealed a gloomy spiral staircase at the bottom of which stood a bright chromium-plated food vending machine. Lili discovered that for the price of 12p., this robot repeatedly offered crisps.

The following morning an unexpected ray of sunshine woke Doran early, so that I was working with him on the ladder by eight o'clock. Lili sat beside us eating a bowl of muesli and I thought Alison must have started writing cards because I hadn't seen her since breakfast. It occurred to me that she might have collected the post.

'Lili, keep Doran walking towards you a moment.'

I ran upstairs. Alison was lying in my bed which must have been the first available place to hide. She was mostly buried by the duvet but she pushed a hand holding an envelope towards me.

'I can guess it's the grant,' I said. 'You weren't accepted. Stay here, concentrate on breathing.'

'I just want to die,' she answered from deep under the covers. 'I don't know how to accept failure.'

I slipped back downstairs to find Lili feeding Doran the last of her muesli. Half an hour later Alison appeared without her shoes. 'Do you like wearing bare feet?' Lili said.

'Yes, it's comforting. It helps when I'm unhappy.'

'Do your feet talk?'

'I don't know. They've never been asked.'

'Well they should be.' Lili bent down to address them. 'Hello, does Alison look after you?' she asked.

Since Alison's feet had no emotional involvement with tropical rain forests they could talk without embarrassment. Doran followed their arguments with Lili, up and down his ladder for the rest of the morning.

We had a week to go before the evaluation. We were watching Doran slowly increase from four to five independent steps; the last took a long time to be established. I could see that five steps would put him up amongst the walkers whereas four still gave the impression of a gradual fall.

During one of our last evenings on the ladder I had success showing Doran a set of slides left over from some art history lectures I used to give. I found myself falling into a flamboyant style. My captive student was evidently enjoying himself; he'd been saturated in Renaissance paintings from an early age and liked recognizing old favourites. Alison walked out of the room and came back several times, finally she said, 'You can't teach him that.'

'What? You sound like George.'

'There's no such thing as good and bad art. It's just a question of individual taste.'

I forgot where I was and burst out, 'Nonsense, good art reflects nature, it's alive. Bad art is dead, it deadens the spirit. It's a subtle killer. It makes no demands, it seals the air out of your imagination.'

'Don't lecture me; I'm not one of your art students.'

'Look, my life has turned out unpredictably and I'm glad; besides I like lecturing.' I began to laugh.

'You don't know anything about being bitter.'

'Do what you can do well, Alison; your time will come.'

'But what can I do well?'

'Make me a cup of tea, you fool,' I said affectionately.

The day before we left, we went to spend a marathon day with a friend who'd been patterning from the first. Her name was Barbara Frost and she had a son, Daniel, who was a few months younger than Doran. When they'd first met, Doran could hardly crawl and Daniel was walking. Now for the four seconds it took Doran to walk five steps there was equality between them.

We were early for our flight which was delayed four hours. When we eventually got into the plane, holding Doran and Lili back in their seats seemed like a full time job, but restraining Alison was impossible.

The removal of safety belts gave the signal for Doran's long self-imposed marathon round the aisles. Lili went ahead to introduce him and show him the toilets. The heat was uncomfortable, so since she hated clothes at the coolest of times, her knickers and shoes were quickly abandoned somewhere en route. The air hostess found the shoes which I put in my bag, but we never saw the knickers again.

Judith drove us to the Chestnut Hill Hotel which showed still more signs of wear and tear from children, but was just as friendly. Lili soon made friends with a South African girl of her own age whose sister was on the programme. The friendship had many charming aspects except for one thing, Lili's four-year-old friend was already an ingrained racist, and very persuasive.

'Mummy, Lisa says it must be awful to be black.'

'Lili, if there wasn't so much prejudice in the world it would be lovely. Ask André's father – he's black.'

André's father roared with laughter.

'Do you have a racial problem, Lili?'

Francis appeared looking for Susan, 'Go on, Lili, climb on to his knee, he's got the power.'

While we were waiting in the clinic wondering how Doran would walk, he saw a small girl balancing unsteadily ahead of him and felt the impulse to run after her.

'Five, six, seven steps, man!' Rosalind had the habit of appearing from nowhere. 'You can certainly chase girls.'

Doran's height was now increasing at ninety-one percent of normal rate, while his head and chest were both growing at four hundred percent which was an incredible change. We went downstairs to the equipment room. Without waiting to be asked, Doran pulled himself up by the overhead ladder and sped backwards and forwards along it in a superb cross pattern. Rosalind drew a breath, 'I've never seen a child walk the overhead ladder so well.'

In fact neither had Alison nor I.

'The guy's a showman,' said Judith. 'He should do his programme at the London Palladium.'

We knew that the next six months were to be crtitical for turning Doran into a walker.

While we were waiting for the new programme we heard a couple talking about their honeymoon and privately wished them well. Gradually we discovered that at least fifty percent of the families, who didn't seem like newlyweds, were wondering if and when they were also having honeymoons. When I saw Anne Ball, who was an English member of staff, I asked her if the word had an American meaning I'd misunderstood.

'No,' she said, 'it's got an Institutes meaning. We give kids a holiday, for their benefit, usually around the end of their second year on the programme.'

'Does that mean Doran will have one?'

'I think he's down for a honeymoon at the end of January. Ros will tell you today.'

The honeymoon was dependent upon Doran's success with his new programme which was in Judith's terms 'pretty wild'.

'All Doran needs to become a truly independent walker is an opportunity to walk,' said Ros, 'so, he is to begin with a minimum of twenty-five periods to walk by himself, and one marathon day of walking opportunities. As his walking improves we will give him more time off the ladder. Your goal is to have Doran walking four kilometres on the overhead ladder and to walk four metres non-stop by himself. You'll need to put up more ladders.'

'It's amazing what fits in my cottage.'

'There are one or two other things you have to squeeze in there, Mrs Scotson,' Ros smiled. 'I see Doran is scheduled for quite a vestibular programme to improve the quality of his walking.'

We had been lectured on the connection between developing the vestibular part of the brain for balance and to orientate a child in space. The four techniques they proposed for Doran, were vertical pirouetting head up, vertical pirouetting head down, vertical rotation and rolling. We returned to the equipment room to see some examples of precisely what they had in mind. Vertical pirouetting head up involved strapping Doran into a swivel chair. Pirouetting head down meant putting straps round his boots and then suspending him upside down from a hook in the ceiling. Vertical rotation was even more bizarre. We had to fix a large round board like a tabletop into the wall; Doran was to be harnessed to the board which was then revolved by hand. Rolling, simply meant Doran lay down and was rolled twenty-five times backwards and forwards between two people. All the movement had to be done clockwise and anti-clockwise. A third of it was to be spent spinning slowly, a third with abrupt acceleration and deceleration, and a third with gradual acceleration. We were to do three weeks intensive vestibular as soon as possible in order that Doran would have the information for his ladder walking.

'Where will you put the stuff?' Judith enquired.

'In the back bedroom. It will be Doran's own private fairground – he'll absolutely love it.'

'Did you hear that, Doran?' Alison asked. 'You lucky boy!'

Doran looked more dubious but we swept him upstairs for the overview before he could comment.

We ate a picnic supper at Kennedy airport. Lili kept skipping about offering hers to any of the other passengers to whom she took a fancy. I looked again and noticed she had no shoes. They were neatly left under a bench at the other end of the lounge. Doran became so excited at the prospect of take-off, I wondered if the return flight would be as riotous as the one out, but once we were in the air both children slept.

Alison exalted over the sunrise. 'You're beginning to sound more like the artist,' I said. 'Enjoy your sunrise; I have these notes to look over. It'll be some time before my son also rises.'

'Linda, how can you make puns about Doran when we're actually riding on the back of Apollo.'

'Alison, I need someone to donate Doran a hundred feet of ladder.'

Diana brought us home. We'd left the cottage tidy although not more than superficially clean. I wanted to drink as many cups of weak tea as possible and plan the new programme. Alison felt almost ill with anticlimax and a kind of cultural shock. Everything in England seemed suddenly much smaller and slower. She wandered about miserably or flung herself down on the grass holding her head. On Monday Alison was still very disorientated. Our loyal friends had arrived to hear that for the next six months at least there was going to be no more patterning. While they attempted an improvized programme, which included entertaining Lili, I steadily phoned carpenters. Peter was haymaking and very busy, James was away. I went down a long list, until I found a very sympathetic person who seemed unruffled by the idea of vertical rotation. Then I set out to discover someone who would provide a swivel chair and ladders for the garden. The ladders for the house had to be hand made. Together they would run from the front gate, round the front room, up the stairs, round the bedroom, through the kitchen and out down the garden to the apple tree. I took Doran to a ladder manufacturer in the next town and after he'd been on a guided tour of the workshops, we were promised a hundred feet of ladder. My carpenter offered to make up the indoor ladder as soon as the wood arrived but suggested that it was cheaper and quicker to find someone he could teach and then let them get on with it. At this point Alison surfaced. She was returned to a state of shock when she realized the entire house was to be filled with ladders.

'Doran's got to be free to move anywhere he wants,' I insisted. 'It's my house and I don't mind.'

'But we'll be bumping into them all the time. We won't be able to move.'

'We'll learn to duck; besides that's not the point. The point is Doran.'

'Doran, Doran, Doran – I'm sick of Doran.'

'I suppose you are; you've worked too hard. Why don't you set yourself a time to leave and tell CSV; you won't feel half so trapped.'

'But that seems too much like failure.'

'But you were going to leave at the end of September – to go to Edinburgh to do your Ph.D.'

'Exactly. Now I've nowhere to go.' She paused. 'At any rate I can find you someone who'll help build the ladders.'

She phoned an old friend of hers called Paul Willis.

Paul came. After a short apprenticeship to our carpenter he laboured without any apparent rest, making ladders by day and 'bits' cards by night. As the ladders went up Doran ran down them to watch his new hero at work. We chopped the legs off the patterning table and carried it out to the shed. I had no idea when it might be needed again.

I could now fall into bed and sleep off my long postponed jet lag. Paul and Alison worked until the early hours of each morning and at the end of a week we could start the new programme.

Doran was saddened to see his friend go; he stood mournfully at the gate waving bye bye. Over the week he had learned to copy Paul's thumbs up sign, and as the car reached the bend in the lane they exchanged this parting salute. Alison decided to stay on until the end of the month, but made no definite plans for her future.

Our carpenter needed a large bearing to fix the wood for Doran's vertical rotation to the wall, and we were still waiting for it. Then Bert came to discuss the cost of the work. She wasn't happy about the prospect of fund raising over Christmas, and talked seriously about facing the prospect of not getting back to Philadelphia. However black things looked, not going back was unacceptable to me.

One of my oldest patterners and friends, Barbara Frost and her son Daniel arrived on Doran's third birthday, so did a huge lorryload of ladders for the garden. Barbara and I climbed up on to the lorry with the children, and Doran cheerfully gave the thumbs up sign each time a ladder was lowered on to the front lawn. Barbara said, 'It's a good birthday for Doran, but you seem to have a lot of problems, and you'll miss Alison.'

We thanked the men and climbed down. Then, ducking under the ladder inside the front door, we followed Doran through the house.

Lili and Alison had made a birthday tea. Doran looked at the cake and gave the thumbs up sign again.

'That's the spirit, Doran,' said Alison.

'It's yours now too, remember?' I said. 'It's called winning through.'

Alison lifted her cup.

'Here's to the day. Eat a slice of good art and don't argue,' she replied.

14

—————— ✳ ——————

ALISON DECIDED to stay in the village and work at Jean's farm while she waited for the results of a VSO application. CSV sent another candidate called Sue Tooey; she was a music graduate whose humour and appearance had a boyishness in common with Alison. They liked each other immediately. Sue had no difficulty establishing rapport with Doran or the ladders, but when she attempted to show Lili her violin Lili contrived to fall on top of it. Their initial relationship was not easy.

The question of Lili's education frequently found its way into conversation; I had not yet made up my mind what to do about it. She felt so much part of our daily life I couldn't imagine the house without her. Then, just before her fifth birthday, her need to have a new form of independence became clear; she moved out of my bed and into her own room. I remembered the school we used to creep round. Lili was anxious to start there immediately, so the problem solved itself.

Now that Doran could climb in and out of a bed he was allowed one of his own beside mine, tucked underneath the ladder that ran round the room. He could get up and start walking while I dressed. The ladder on the stairs provided more of a symbolic connection between ladders than a physical aid to walking; he swung and slithered down to the living room.

We had to supply continuous motivation for the next four months, Doran was meant to earn a short privilege every fifteen minutes. Although he walked obligingly along the ladders his independent walking didn't improve. He had an inability to

February 1982. With Sue, his first four metres in Crawley
shopping arcade. Hands up in the primary balance position.

Neil and Daphne fix Doran in the respirator.

centre himself and he lost his balance easily. As my desperation was rising the carpenter appeared with the central part for the vertical rotation device and a huge circular piece of wood. He covered the wood with carpet and fastened on a harness made at the local saddlery. Then he drilled into the wall of Lili's bedroom and hoisted the whole thing in place.

Doran was remarkably patient. We tried various angulations of his body to get him in while the wheel slipped clockwise and anti-clockwise.

'Has he done this before?' asked the carpenter.

'No never; that's why he needs it so much. Most children are thrown around when they are babies; he missed his opportunity.'

We spun Doran slowly. As his feet were again replaced by his head we could see that his smile was still intact. The vertical pirouetting head down was another matter. We put a pile of cushions underneath the hook, hoisted him up and spun him.

Doran didn't see himself ideally in this role but when we lowered him to the floor he put up his thumb. He wasn't saying he enjoyed it; he was saying few people would have the guts to survive it. After this the swivel chair could only be a success. Our problem was keeping Doran straight; if he wasn't, the information would be wrong. Whichever way we tried him in the chair he slumped. In the end it was taking more time to tie him in and take him out than to turn him round.

'Why don't you use that baby seat you have in the hedge by the car?' someone said.

I puzzled over what she meant and then a memory of the seat came back. It was a stiff backed hard plastic chair which had been kindly given to me at a time when Doran couldn't bend at the waist. I had never been able to bring it in, now the object had a perfect purpose.

Rolling Doran across the floor and back, twenty-five times, as if he were a lump of clay we expected to gradually elongate, soon removed the knees of Sue's jeans. It was difficult to perform in a skirt. Lili had been sorting through jumble and produced a pair of my old black cord trousers. I put them on. They both approved.

'You look good in them,' Sue remarked, 'less like a mother.'

'Being a mother is always a sign that one's made love, you know; and love is what all the rock songs are about.'

'I was joking.'

Doran rolled awkwardly, his arms and legs flew out.

'He needs to be in a bag,' Sue said.

Since there was no suitable sack, we bound Doran hand and foot with some pairs of old stockings. He looked diffident but was uncomplaining; he hadn't known physical freedom long enough to see this as imprisonment. Before long he refused to start without the security of bondage.

When Lili came home from school she rushed upstairs to the circus that was also her bedroom. Doran tottered across the floor in the interludes between acts, carrying toys from one person to another and watching his intelligence cards. Lili found a large brown bear who didn't walk very well and needed to follow Doran's route through the vestibular programme.

Most people who came worried a little understandably about Doran's digestion; I used to swear that he was in no danger of throwing up. I knew that some brain injured children suffered continuous nausea. This of course would put them off the food their loving parents were trying to get them to eat. Doran's own appetite had if anything improved since we started throwing him about. After a particularly large lunch I squeezed him into the harness and we began turning the wheel. At the third revolution the undigested meal appeared, whistled passed our ears and landed on the floor. We cleared it up and went on. By the time we had finished the activities it was pushing ten o'clock, which meant Lili had gone to sleep to the roll of the wheel and the squeaks of the swivel chair.

The next day while I was picking herbs from my wilderness of a back garden, George came up.

'You're using your washing machine late, aren't you?'

'Am I?' I said blankly. 'I can't remember.'

'You ought to get it seen to; it shouldn't make a noise like that.'

226

I realized as he disappeared that the noise had been Doran's vertical rotation.

The vestibular programme was clearly working. Doran could walk across the room without tripping over a speck of dust, and the better he walked the more he enjoyed walking. Sue also noticed that she was developing fine muscles in her arms. One evening the neighbour at the end of the terrace came round to complain about the noise. He had no idea what could cause such a powerful rumbling unless we were drilling for oil in the foundations? I wondered whether showing him Doran tied up like a human sacrifice would clarify the matter. The man didn't want to know any details he merely suggested I fix a silencer on to whatever gadget was causing the trouble.

Lili had been given a tape recorder by her godfather so that he could send her tapes with stories read by himself. If she woke early in the morning she would put a tape on and listen to it before she came into my room. The story she most often chose was the *Specklety Hen* by Alison Uttley. That hen would invariably cluck its way into my bedroom and take over my dream. Sue who slept above Lili knew each word by heart. While we were shifting Doran through his vestibular we began to quote it to each other.

When Doran fell asleep we put straps round his boots and began to spin him. He sighed, licked his lips and stayed asleep, until we'd taken him down and turned him in the chair.

As Sue began to see Lili's jokes she could recognize her as a friend. In the same way once Lili realized she wasn't being taken over seriously she included Sue in her household and their understanding grew.

Alison came at the weekends. She had a motor scooter and could do some shopping for us. Anybody passing Diana's shop would take a list, and in this way we maintained our provisions.

By the end of the three weeks' vestibular, Doran's walking was satisfactorily straighter. Being set free under the ladders again seemed like living in a mansion after so long in one room. The ladders were very substantial; most children, including Lili, spent their time walking the top of them while Doran chased underneath. He could work up quite a speed, but he could also walk as if he were moving through treacle.

Lili and Sue spent a lot of time drawing or painting together. The more Sue did, the more interested she became. She began asking me all sorts of technical questions; finally I was tempted to produce some oil paints and find an old bottle of white spirit. When Alison came at the weekend Sue was making pictures while Doran tracked up and down to see them develop. Sue wanted Alison to try, and suggested they both work on the same piece of hardboard but their styles conflicted. After some controversy I found a box of oil pastels and put them on the table. So, over the following evenings I became the only person not painting, even Doran began walking with a paint-brush between his teeth (or in his chip bag). When he reached the end of his trip there was a pallet and a large piece of white paper pinned up for him to streak with colour.

One evening, after Doran and Lili were bathed and in bed and we'd cleaned up the house, Sue said, 'What's in you, Linda? You don't smoke, you don't drink, you don't go out, your house is hung with pictures, but you don't paint.'

'True.'

'You don't even get angry.'

'Sometimes I do,' I said. 'More often I question.'

By the end of the week the new art was plastered all over the walls, its students were well entrenched. Some uncomfortable frustrated energy began to assert itself in me. As a last resort I walked through to Alison who was lighting a cigarette by the door.

'Do you mind if I have that?' I said, and snatched it almost before she could answer.

I ran down the garden and leant against the back of the shed inhaling deeply. It was over twelve years since I'd smoked. I drew the nicotine down to my toes and felt the pain dissipate in a rush of light-headed energy. Afterwards I plunged into the morass of my abandoned life, most of which resided in the depth of the shed that had once been my studio. I reappeared with an armful of canvases.

'What are you doing?'

'What I have to.'

I turned the canvases round, fixed them to stretchers and covered them with white emulsion paint. Then I began to work using a mixture of oil pastels, white spirit rags, brushes and knives.

While Doran was on his ladders I propped up a canvas at one end; my sheer concentration brought him swiftly down to interfere. I then had to pick the whole thing up and rush back to the beginning. As a way of making pictures it was quite extraordinary. I hung the unfinished canvases on different parts of the wall and from time to time I would leap on a chair and make a few quick strokes. Afterwards I'd take a stack of 'bits' cards and show them to him with the same sort of speed, moving backwards as I went.

Doran's walking off the ladder increased in confidence but he couldn't yet get across the room. When he was tired we gave him some extra time in the swivel chair and sometimes from the hook.

Sue had a birthday in early December. We decided that if we put wooden boards down on top of the ladders they would make tables without inhibiting Doran's hands. So, with the provision that Doran must be stimulated to keep on walking, we could have a party. We invited old friends and plenty of children. Many of the people I knew well lived in London, and had only the vaguest idea of what kept me locked away in the country. I wasn't sure if they'd understand or even approve of Doran's programme.

When the day came, visitors streamed in climbing under ladders and putting down bottles of wine on the kitchen table. Doran greeted our guests from his vertical position and ran from room to room pursued by children. Gradually the old questions came up one by one. 'Wasn't it tiring for Doran?' 'Wasn't Lili jealous?' 'Didn't I get any time for myself?' I answered that doing the programme was my choice, that actually I had been painting, and that I didn't need the wine. Doran didn't get tired, Lili didn't want to be left out but she wasn't jealous, and – yes – I had suddenly started smoking the occasional cigarette but we couldn't in front of Doran because it reduced the oxygen in the atmosphere. Having run this gauntlet, the going was easier.

I had become so used to being understood by the people around me; it was strange to be caught doing something that my less conventional friends found difficult to accept. I knew it was unfair because there was no way I could communicate the background in such short intervals of time without sounding either too flippant or too intense.

Some time after the children were in bed a small group remained in the kitchen and I was affectionately pressed with invitations to dinner. Alison offered me a cigarette.

'I wish I'd known you before all this.'

'About five years ago perhaps,' I said, 'when you were still at school?'

'What will you do when you stop?'

'Go on helping other brain injured kids.'

'Won't you have had enough of it?'

'Come on now, I'm obsessional.'

'But what about painting?'

'I don't know. Maybe I don't paint well enough to justify doing it. Maybe I can do both; it's too early to guess.'

The party had been a success; we survived it without anti-climax. During the following week Alison had her interview for VSO. Two days afterwards she phoned to say the VSO had wanted nurses and teachers, not biology graduates.

'Everything I touch now fails.'

'Look how much better Doran is,' I said.

'That was when I was winning; I'd better not come near him in future.'

She went off to Jean's to milk the goats. All I could think of was sending her flowers. She rang back to thank me.

'I've got some savings; I shall advertise for someone to go with me to do research, and if that doesn't work I'll go by myself.'

Soon after this it began to snow, and freeze, and snow again. The school taxi couldn't get through.

'I can go by myself, mummy,' Lili said.

I allowed her to try until I realized she was in the distance and not going to turn round without a serious alternative. Eventually she accepted the idea of bringing buckets of snow into the house so that Doran could walk down his ladders towards a group of snowmen.

As the snowmen rose, melted and were rebuilt again, Doran's independent walking became more vigorous.

Just as we were wondering what to do about supplies Alison appeared at the door with two carrier bags of groceries.

'It's lovely out there, the air's so clear,' she said. 'Can I stay the night?'

When we turned on the taps at breakfast there was no cold water. George told us he'd had a warning of this a week ago from the water company. I looked under the mat and produced a muddy card.

'What about the snow?' Alison asked.

'It's cold,' I said.

'And wet!'

'Brilliant, Alison. To quote your own word, "brilliant".'

We filled the kettle with snow and had our tea. The snow was beautiful but confining.

'Can we go to the Isle of Wight for Christmas, mummy?' Lili was looking through the window. 'It doesn't snow there.'

If Doran had made his interim report goal it would be possible to do three marathon walking days all together. Doran subscribed to this idea by making all his goals ahead of schedule. 'He can go on a walking tour of the island,' said Alison. 'I'll pack him a rucksack.'

We arranged to travel on Christmas Eve. The snow was still thick but the taxi took us to the station without incident. The driver kept glancing in his mirror to watch me masking Doran. Once in the train we took turns taking Doran along its length and letting him walk a few independent steps between us. The other passengers couldn't make up their minds whether we were simply fooling about or whether there was some reason behind this madness. I concluded that the balance he had to

231

use as the train shook from side to side was good for his vestibular growth.

The Solent obliged by being rough and the heaving of the boat provided still better vestibular, but by the time we reached the island we could see the grass was green. Lili had been right about the snow.

We had developed the art of walking backwards to catch Doran as he was released. When I pursued this tactic round the house I discovered that my parents had a remarkable array of breakable objects. My mother borrowed a high chair and wedged a mattress for him between the two divan beds which were intended for Lili and I. In fact most of the nights seemed to be spent exchanging beds. There was a park in front of the house in which we all went walking, sending Doran on from one of us to the next like a game of football. It was the first time he'd ever been outside taking steps. By Boxing Day my father was saying, 'Have you noticed how that little boy's come on?'

Doran was more assured, three days of living as a freely upright person had given him a new view of himself. We had a railway carriage to ourselves coming back, and he walked across it fearlessly.

Lili had opted to stay behind in the green and pleasant isle until the end of her holidays. The mainland was still covered with snow. Doran was not happy to see his ladders again but we had hardly put down our cases before there was a call to invite him to a fund-raising disco and concert. Since the invitation was further baited with the offer of a lift, I accepted on everyone's behalf.

We kept the fire in all night for warmth; the wind pushed under the door and through the cracks around the rotten window frames. It was ideal to keep moving. Doran saved up his chips for the privilege of taking us all to the disco. He was having a light tea on the ladders to tide him over for the big event, when the lights went out. We groped for matches which led us in turn to candles and candlesticks. The new light provided shadow pictures and allowed Doran to finish off his meal with snacks of toasted cheese. Sue put a candle in the window so that when our lift arrived there would be some indication that we were still at home.

Doran walked into the hall in his customary fashion, while his entourage struggled backwards to catch him. Our seats were at a table near the stage. My son consumed a plate of food that would have overpowered a lesser mortal and applauded jokes from a highly sexist comic. One in particularly poor taste arrived when Doran had just stuffed his mouth full of food; the comic had egg and cress sandwich showered towards him.

A young girl who'd been singing in the concert decided to dance on the stage. When some other children got up to join her Doran fell off his chair in his agitation to follow suit. Alison picked him up and he staggered towards the stage; he was after all the guest of honour. We followed lifting him to his feet when necessary. Doran held out his hand to the girl and smiled.

'Cor, cor, ga, ga,' he remarked, and with that they were dancing together.

'He's cute,' she said. 'Can I keep him?'

She did, until *Auld Lang Syne* marked the end of his evening. He went to sleep in the car, cuddled up with Sue. From time to time deep bubbling laughter broke through his dreams.

Alison spent the next day carrying out her new year's resolution by writing to various missions in the tropical rain belt. Working for a mission would at least give her a start in the right area. Meanwhile we had grown used to her help and she stayed with us. There was a slight thaw about the time Lili came home and no more difficulties about her getting to school except being up on time for the knock at the door in the morning. Although we were still using the vestibular techniques occasionally, they were no longer part of the official programme. I felt that if we were going to push Doran into walking four metres non-stop before the end of February when the honeymoon was projected, he needed to have better balance.

We tried taking him out round the local supermarkets which

were at least warm and dry. As usual one of us walked in front of him and one walked behind. When Lili was with us she pushed the trolley; if Doran did well he pushed the trolley and Lili climbed into it. We collected far more stuff than we needed and had to go round again to replace most of it on the shelves. Doran tottered towards us, his arms lifted in the primary balance role. It was good but it had to be better. The Institutes confirmed that he needed more vestibular. I would have to explain to George that my washing machine had broken again.

Since Doran's walking programme did not always oppose his social life, provided his routine was acceptable, we could agree to his accompanying Lili to the birthday party of one of her friends. On the afternoon in question it had started snowing again and regardless of the disappointment I was loath to go. Sue wanted some excitement.

'I thought you were a tomboy. Are you too frightened to drive?'

Alison went the other way and insulted my car.

'I wouldn't take that old crate anywhere,' she said. 'The steering's terrible and the clutch is slipping.'

'It's a Volvo, the car's built for bad weather; otherwise the Swedes couldn't manage,' I cried.

Doran zoomed down the ladder by the front door looking for his coat and Lili said, 'Why didn't you stay with grannie! There's no snow on the Isle of Wight.'

So I decided we were going. The party was in a house we'd crawled over so many times we could still see ourselves on all fours coming round the settee. Being upright there gave me a giddy pleasure. Doran was delighted to find the father of the household at home and walked towards him with a manly pride in his new stature. We watched, sipping tea and feeling unnecessary.

'Wait a moment!' I paced out the floor. 'He's done it! Doran's just walked five metres.'

He did it again and again. He could calculate just how far he could go until his knees buckled, and placed his falls very accurately.

He made his entrée into the dining room several times, hurling himself exuberantly against the table while paper cups overflowed and oatcakes rained to the floor. Walking had ceased to be hard work as long as everything was within a five metre stretch; it was quicker than creeping.

Alison had been outside to smoke. 'Have you seen the weather?' she asked. The snow was thick and drifting heavily over the car. Regretfully we departed. I still saw my car as capable of driving safely over a glacier. As we climbed the last hill home the wheels began to spin, the clutch slipped, while to add insult to injury, several British cars passed us with no apparent trouble.

'You forget this is a Swedish car,' said Alison. 'It's custom built for mild English winters.'

Lili cuddled Doran while Alison and Sue braved the elements to begin digging round the wheels. It took another five minutes for the clutch to burn out. The car behind chivalrously offered to drive us down the other side of the hill and home.

Doran escaped down his ladders looking almost relieved to see them again. Sue made tea; we had all decided it was better to celebrate Doran walking five metres than bemoan the fate of the car. We put loud music on the stereo and did some limbo dancing under the ladders.

I had a friend who was an excellent mechanic as well as being a saint, and when the weather cleared he towed the car back and replaced the clutch. Once we were mobile we spent a week taking Doran about town to assure ourselves that the walking was more than a lucky chance. Then I contacted the Institutes who declared we were officially on honeymoon until March. I also rang Judith to tell her the glorious news; she suggested Alison, Doran and I travel a week early and stay with them in Vermont. The fund was low but Alison's parents made her a present of the trip; she saw it as a kind of farewell holiday. Replies had begun to come in from various denominations of Christian missions; she wondered if she should declare herself to be a Baptist, a Methodist or a Catholic.

'What about one of the "Non religious Godly",' I suggested.

'But they all want me to be on their side.'

'Okay, sound as if you're on the brink of conversion – that's true enough – you don't know to what as yet.'

That week Alison put her advertisement in the *New Scientist* for a young biologist willing to accompany her to the tropical rain forests. Bert appeared on the way to a committee meeting for the Fund. 'Well love,' she said, 'someone will have to pull their finger out soon if we're ever to get you there. Have you heard the rumours about Freddie Laker? If he goes bust the cost of air fares will rocket.'

Freddie Laker did go bust. Then money arrived from a friend who gave a large, very expensive dinner party in aid of Doran. This, plus money raised through the thousand club and the disco, scraped us through. We had enough to buy tickets from British Airways.

The honeymoon wasn't intended to be a passive affair. We were meant to be giving Doran the time of his life both physically and academically. This was quite difficult to achieve on Ashdown Forest in February. Two surprise events occurred. Both Magda and Moe were getting married and we were all invited to the weddings; besides this we arranged to stay a week in London with Lili's godfather and his family, and at least a week with my parents. I had decided that, although Doran was off his programme as such, since he was now a walker the one thing he must do was to walk. He had incredible energy but no sense of his own safety. I strove diligently to avoid him spending the better part of his honeymoon having his cuts sewn up at the local hospital.

Alison had sorted through the countless replies to her advertisement. Her first client was coming down from Glasgow to visit us. She took Sue with her to pick him up at the station. When they arrived back I was on the floor in the most domestic of roles, changing Doran's nappy.

'I'd hoped they'd find you looking a little more dignified, Doran,' I remarked as I introduced him. We chatted tentatively about train journeys and brain injured children and then Murray said, 'Where's the mother?'

'Who?' I asked.

'Doran's mum.'

'It's a riot, Murray,' I said, 'but I have to confess I am.'

Murray looked at Alison in mock accusation. 'You said she was a poor widow lady!'

'In a manner of speaking she is,' Alison said. 'I wanted you to think I was working for someone respectable.'

Doran was quick to notice that Murray was tall, thin and fair. He behaved as if he thought the young man was a personal gift for his consumption. This attitude combined with their similarity of appearance contrived to make most people assume he was Doran's father, and since Murray was obviously with Alison she had the dubious honour of being credited his mother.

When we took Murray to Moe's wedding some friends of the bride's relatives watched Doran, assumed the wrong parentage, and began, 'It's a shame about their little boy.'

'No, really he's doing well,' I said.

'It must be difficult for his mother.'

'No, they have an excellent relationship.'

'They say children like that are very loving.'

Doran had climbed up to the fruit bowl and was passing chinese gooseberries down to Murray.

'I expect he likes music. They're supposed to be musical.'

'That's Down's Syndrome,' I said, 'but actually "they" are all hurt individual people. There's a neurological programme to change the destiny of kids like that. Doran's on it and he's getting better.'

'His father seems to understand him,' they answered, and moved away.

Doran and Murray were peeling and eating the fruit. I realized that Doran's injury was going to precede his personality, at least for a while.

Then I noticed that Doran was about to have a good time trying to unwrap the wedding presents. Alison brought him back and started to dance. Someone else asked me what I did.

'A kind of construction work. It involves flying to New York every six months.'

'How interesting. You're an architect?'

'Figuratively speaking, yes.'

'You mean a sculptor?'

'That too,' I said, accepting a cigarette. 'What do you do?'

A major problem with the evenings was how to persuade Doran to fall asleep early. He'd been used to pressing on until midnight and he showed no inclination to change his routine. We finally decided it was realistic to take down some of the ladders. This did not prevent us continuing to bend underneath the places where they had been, which looked nearly as extraordinary.

Murray seemed to be more of a poet than a biologist. He took long wet walks through the fields. 'I was standing by the stream, pouring out my sorrow to this horse,' he reported. 'I was reciting him one of my most lugubrious ditties when I saw a great tear fall out of the creature's eye and roll down his cheek.'

Murray and Alison came to some sort of loose arrangement before he went home. She wanted to go to Papua New Guinea and he wanted to go to Africa, but it seemed to be a matter that could be resolved.

I continued to present my brain injured child to the world. We packed up and went to stay in London. If I hadn't known I was being saved by the programme in the first place I would have done so then. Working without a structure broke down the remnants of my immediate reserves; I turned yellowish and seemed compelled to go and pee at every possible opportunity. Friends suggested that either my liver or kidneys were packing up. I debated whether I was still needed on earth and came to the conclusion that I was, in which case I would undoubtedly revive with rest.

We took Doran and Lili round to museums and art galleries. Doran was unconerned by the fact that he fell every five metres and I was rapidly used to making a genuflection every time I had to pick him up. One of the guards in the National Gallery gave him a large wrapped sweet. I explained on his behalf that he couldn't eat it, but would like to save it for Alison who'd gone home to her parents to do some more work on tropical rain forests. Doran produced this delicacy to show to every other guard we passed and I obligingly repeated the story for him until finally a voice said: 'I know, I gave it to him.'

We'd made a complete circuit and I hadn't raised my eyes above the picture frames.

When Lili went out to a rather sophisticated children's entertainment we took Doran to my old art school in Holborn. He was wearing a blue dufflecoat with the collar turned up and looked rather a Toulouse Lautrec figure as he tottered round the palettes and easels. I knew if I mentioned that I went to New York every six months the implication would be that I was having a series of exhibitions or a lover, or both out there; no one connected me with children and certainly not brain injured ones.

We had arranged to meet one of the lecturers I knew well, together with another of his former students and, for the sake of nostalgia, we took Doran to the pub. We found a dark corner and I decided I would tell the management that Doran was a thirty-six-year-old midget if they protested. He lent back assuredly listening to the conversation and looking into his orange juice. I had intended to hold the glass for him, but having observed that this was not common procedure he pushed my hand away and I was forced to watch the perilous journey of the drink to and from his lips.

'Someone once said I fed my children intoxicants,' I remarked. 'I couldn't really criticize them if they could see Doran now.'

The next observation Doran made was that what one evidently did while one was thus drinking was talk, pause, and talk again. For the first time in his life he was producing long burbling sentences of an appropriately drunken quality.

'He looks too much at home in this atmosphere,' I said.

'Could it be you produced the reincarnation of Dylan Thomas?' my friend remarked.

The day we met my mother at Waterloo station, it was particularly cold and bitter. She looked at me as if I had a terminal illness she wasn't supposed to know about.

'I'm aware what I look like,' I said. 'Sue's promised to nurse me until death but I think I'll try a week in bed first.'

Sue came to be my right hand woman. As soon as I was inside the door of the house I kissed my father, took a bath and went upstairs to bed. For the first two days I simply slept; then I looked along my old bookshelves and found a novel by Herman Hesse called *Steppenwolf*. I had bought it thirteen years ago but never felt it was quite the right moment to begin it. This was the first novel I'd looked at for three years and exactly the right one unconsciously saved until now. As I lay reading or sleeping, images passed through my head. I began to scribble lines of poems.

Lili occupied the bed beside me and Doran lay between us; his sleep was still restless but it was easy to get up in the night knowing I had nothing but rest before me all day. No gift could have been more perfect.

The children were taken to the beach, and the cinema, and in the evening they had the new miraculous thing called television. Doran was a great audience participator; he laughed and clapped at anything that appealed to him. After ten days the prospect of getting up became unexpectedly attractive.

This was pretty much on target for going back to the Institutes, via Vermont. Lili was looking forward to becoming a temporary pupil at the school where my mother used to teach. We left them both in the classroom while my father drove us to the station. He was one of the élite few who didn't seem to see anything much wrong with Doran at all; they met personality to personality. 'I wish I was going with you,' he said.

Alison's parents had offered to take us to Heathrow which meant we didn't have to worry about getting lost.

We had a little party the day before during which Doran ate a lot of grapes. He woke in the night with a full nappy which I attributed regretfully to the grapes. Before we left he'd had it again, this time it necessitated a complete change of clothing. My guilt about the grapes increased.

'How many did he have?' asked Alison. 'They must have all passed through him by now.'

Feeling relatively sanguine about this estimate and dressed rather more formally than one might expect to go off on a jaunt with a three-year-old brain injured child, I climbed into the very smart clean car Alison's father was driving. Two miles down the road it was apparent Doran was going to be sick. I held him forward. We stopped the car, cleaned out the worst and put some newspaper down. Another few miles on loud rumbling noises heralded more diarrhoea. To save time we held out against changing him until it was absolutely vital. By now the inside of the car left much to be desired and I was wondering if Doran had kidney failure.

'He's got all the same symptoms,' I said. 'It could be nothing more than an upset stomach, but I've never known Doran have something that wasn't serious.'

Alison's parents remained stalwart in their support and gave me no indication that the nauseous state of the back of the car was at all untoward.

'I don't know whether we should go to America or Guy's Hospital,' I said. 'And then if we *are* going to Heathrow, won't we be too late for the flight anyway?'

Fortunately Alison's father had the sort of character that persuaded him to be early for appointments. Despite the setbacks we arrived at the British Airways terminal in time to take Doran to the toilets. The staff directed us to a room for nursing mothers from which it was said it would be possible to call a doctor. While I stripped and washed Doran, Alison tried to find out from the attendant, who for some reason couldn't speak English, the whereabouts of a doctor.

In the middle of the ablutions Doran unexpectedly began to laugh.

'Just a minute,' I called out, 'I think he's over the crisis; he's enjoying himself.'

The desperate look had lifted from him and his colour returned; perhaps it was just as well that we hadn't found a doctor. I left Doran with the Geddes family and checked in our luggage. When I came back Doran was travelling up and down the escalators holding Brian's hand. We kissed goodbye and they went off, Jean carrying a small packet of Doran's wet clothes as a memento of the experience.

We had brought every conceivable necessity, including food and drink, so that the news that there had been a strike amongst British Airways ground staff was the least of our worries. Anyway, substitute packed meals were handed out in the departure lounge. These were designed to appease; they contained smoked salmon and champagne.

After take-off, two passengers exchanged places with us so that we could have the extra leg room in front of the emergency exit. The third passenger was a smart businessman who was no friend of children. This was not a drawback as far as Doran was concerned; he went to great trouble to offer his companions pieces of squashed banana and half of his wholemeal biscuits. Although the crisis was over, visits to the toilet persisted; I must have changed Doran six times in seven hours. We spread out our picnic at the feet of the businessman who tried to protect himself with his brief case. The sight of the three of us sitting on the floor was a magnet for restless children. We also provided a fountain of orange juice and spring water.

The British Airways steward maintained he had never seen anything like it in his career, but he was happy to accept a biscuit. The businessman mysteriously moved up into 'Club Class'.

When we arrived at Kennedy we were down to our last nappy. Judith wasn't there; she'd been held up in a snow drift in Vermont. We were finally collected, took on more supplies of nappies and with a few necessary pauses we made our way north above the snow line.

Doran flung himself into an American lifestyle as if there were no going back. He was already walking more than five metres, and stretched out his vocabulary of handshakes and thumbs up signs with the words 'bye bye' addressed to or about anything in the act of leaving. This gave him the chance to make a meaningful contribution to conversation. Whether or not it was America, Americans, or a new confidence in Doran himself, it was clear now that in the United States this week, his personality was going ahead of him.

15

---❋---

JUDITH GAVE a small party in Doran's honour. He made friends first with a composer, and then with her husband who was a sculptor. Alison and I seemed to have finally contracted the stomach problem and were less available. The sculptor invited Doran round to the Art Department at Bennington College and suggested we join them. Once there, Doran considered he was now the complete student and had to be dragged out of barrels of clay and troughs of printing ink.

Later in the week we drove further north to visit a friend of Judith's whose severely injured son had just begun a programme. The snow was banked up along the roadside and when we stopped for refreshment I saw that signs exhorting one not to shoot young bears were glued to the washroom doors. Cindy had a wooden house and work took place largely in the basement. Doran found himself staring at someone else's patterning table and a wide slide to encourage a child who could move his arms and legs to connect any random kicking with forward progression. Doran tried the slide while Zachery was on the patterning table; he also joined in the vigorous applause as Zachery took his turn.

'Once upon a time,' I said as I tried to prevent Doran tearing the place apart, 'my son couldn't move.'

On the long drive to Philadelphia I remembered I hadn't filled in the revisit report. This was normally done with the critical seriousness and attention to detail it officially merited.

In high spirits we argued out the issues of what Doran could or couldn't do. I gave the pen to Alison who maintained she could write in the back of a car without getting sick.

The Chestnut Hill Hotel had changed hands and was in the process of general repairs so its families had to forget their reunion on the landing and select alternative accommodation. It was also a turning point. We had been coming to the Institutes for two years; now we had to choose whether to continue on a six monthly basis, change to annual visits, or settle for a correspondence course.

Whatever happened the group was meeting for the last time. There were a lot of large inflated Easter Rabbits about the clinic, and Francis and Susan appeared with a bunch of heart-shaped balloons. He paused outside to relate the story of how he got a peanut stuck in his sinuses by taking a deep breath before sneezing.

I couldn't believe that Doran would make the progress he needed unless we maintained our routine. When Rosalind asked us if we thought the results worth the effort all I could say was, 'Compared with the results there was no effort.'

Doran's appearance spoke for itself, which was as well because I was feeling a little regretful about the state of my report. His new programme included creeping, crawling and vestibular every day; four cross patternings, three respiratory patternings and a great deal of walking on the flat. The revisit goal was for him to walk eighteen metres without falling down.

The two year certification ceremony seemed rather embarrassing and very un-English until we actually went through with it. As each family stood up the love that had been demonstrated so practically for the past two years undermined everyone's reserves. Whether we liked it or not our cheeks were wet. After the ceremony we trooped off to a cocktail party given by the School for Human Development. 'Francis, how does it feel to be certified?' I asked.

'In England one is usually certified "insane",' Judith remarked.

'Give over,' he said, 'this is going straight up on my wall beside "Home Sweet Home".'

When we had balanced our glasses and plates delicately enough to get out our cigarettes, the children arrived. At last the families took photographs of each other and exchanged addresses. Doran excelled himself by carrying individual cheese biscuits round the table and dropping them magnanimously on various empty laps.

In two days Alison, Doran and I were home. Sue had transformed the house; it was hard to believe that a week of Doran's programme would reduce this to a memory. We stayed up planning the new schedule. Doran wouldn't sleep; he sat on my knee sucking orange segments dipped in Perrier water. The first thing to be done was to bring in the dismembered patterning table and nail back the legs. The next was to measure Doran for a new respiratory patterning jacket.

Alison was delighted to clear out the rest of the ladders; the ones in the garden were difficult to dislodge.

'Those'll be over four feet in,' George remarked. 'You'll never get them out.' The ground was too hard to reveal otherwise and he went away triumphant. Sue had intended to convert us quickly to English time, but having persuaded her to join us for dinner at midnight, the conversation was reviving enough to keep her up until dawn. Since the house had its own rules, we remained a US outpost until Lili came home. She dispelled these illusions with her first good morning kiss, which arrived an hour after we'd retired to bed.

I bought Doran a new waterproof zip-up suit and took him to creep in the fields. Once there he would either head off towards the banks of the stream or aim straight for a herd of cows. He was unafraid of their scale; when they backed away, he advanced. He would not, however, seriously believe we intended him to crawl, that must be a mistake; it belonged to his past. I explained that crawling was still essential for his neurological reorganization and would improve his respiration. Sue flung herself on to the floor and showed him how easy it was to squeeze behind the sofa. He acknowledged her efforts but demonstrated that his own movement was faster with his stomach off the floor.

He was further surprised to find himself being patterned. The difficulty here was to persuade him to lie passively and not to spring pattern himself at a terrifying rate. When Alison went to a conference on tropical rain forests the old friends who stepped in to help were astonished not only by his physical change but also by the easy affable way in which he recognized them. Alison arrived back glowing. A Dutchman had recruited her to his research team in French Guiana. They planned to leave the following January.

'That's your reward for perseverance,' I said. 'Doran will get his later.'

Doran was struggling with a large blanket under which he was now obliged to crawl to keep himself flat. It was no longer possible to achieve his walking goals inside the house. We often picked Lili up from school and took off for the department stores of Tunbridge Wells. Tea, at the café with bananas and yoghurt, was his incentive. Doran had a preference for playing hide and seek in the lingerie department; if we lost him we had to burrow through rows of nylon slips.

Once or twice a real ten-month-old creeper escaped from its mother to join us and had to be handed back without time for satisfactory explanations. Sue found a copy of the *Guardian* in one of the houses we crept in and saw an advertisement for a post in a music publishing shop in Soho. Out of hundreds of applicants she got the job. We could now give CSV a date at the end of May and wait to see how our household would change. Alison had a future but she found waiting a strain. She suffered a lot from her stomach, spending hours in bed trying to defeat either her body or her mind.

In Doran's interest I had weakened on the subject of zoos. They provided a rich and entertaining walking ground; although I couldn't forget about the cages, at least I could convince myself they were serving a higher moral purpose. One marathon walking day Sue and I decided to explore Drucilla's, a children's zoo with a playground. Doran came out of the reptile house in which he had been lost twice, to catch a glimpse of a small train crammed with exuberant boy scouts. He flew past the monkeys, stumbled, pulled himelf up by the aardvak, took a few more steps fell again and finally reached the wire netting round the track at a fast creep.

We pointed out where the station was and directed him past pelicans and peacocks towards a bridge over the line. From there Lili sighted a wooden fort and slides in the adventure playground.

'Mummy, come on.'

Sue and I were just as enthusiastic, we ignored the sign which said 'Children over fourteen are not permitted to use the equipment'; after all we were helping Doran. It was evident that while the zoo was good for walking, the playground was excellent for creeping; Doran churned up the dust behind him. We saved the train till last. The engine driver waved us on.

'I've watched you working, no need to pay. They deserve the ride!'

'Sue,' I said, 'can you see teams of brain injured children creeping and crawling through custom-built adventure playgrounds with cheerleaders to flash their intelligence cards?'

'I'd work there,' she said.

Lili wanted to buy home-made fudge for Alison and badges for herself and Doran so we called at the shop on our way out.

Alison was in bed with the curtains drawn. I made her a cup of tea and Lili leapt affectionately onto her stomach to offer the fudge. The indigestion and discomfort with life persisted; Alison would appear on cue, pick up an arm and a leg on Doran's left side and proceed through an immaculate five minute patterning while Sue and I sang. Then she'd let go and climb back upstairs without a word.

One fine spring morning she wanted to come with me to help with Doran's creeping in the fields. She ran ahead of him, executed a line of perfect somersaults and sprang up.

'Come on, Dor.'

He did some of his best creeping for a week.

Sue had two days left, 'I can't believe I'm leaving my home.'

'It's always there to come back to, your mark is on Doran.'

'I think I ought to leave a love bite on his neck.'

A few hours later Antonia would be with us. She had a public school background, she was eighteen and was going to Cambridge to read philosophy. She arrived for lunch. We usually had a dish of grains or pasta and a large salad with a bowl of ground cheese nuts and herbs. I added a dish of yoghurt in her honour. It was a rich meal for us.

'It's so nice to eat simply for a change,' she said finishing off the yoghurt. 'What do you usually have for lunch?'

Sue burst out laughing.

'That's it,' I said. 'That's more or less it.'

'Why did you want to do CSV?' Alison asked.

'I've had a good education. I wanted to pay back something to society.'

Antonia watched Doran creeping in the garden.

'Don't you think he's missing some of the necessary pleasures of life?' she said. 'I mean he needs time to pick the flowers.'

'That's a bit premature,' I said.

'I only felt that it would be helpful for you to have some outside advice.'

'The first thing is to observe the programme I've already got from the Institutes.'

Antonia's view of a desirable life style was more in harmony with Lili. They shared a gentle elegance with time to make daisy chains and make believe.

'Is the princess ready for dinner?'

'We can't eat it,' Lili replied. 'It's turned to stone.'

Antonia and I took Doran walking in the play school. The other children were an inspiration especially the naughty ones who wouldn't sit down. We talked about language. Antonia said she believed words should be like beautifully polished glass through which the concept was clearly shown. I spoke in streams of confused images; this was undoubtedly accentuated by the fact that the new programme had banished my opportunity to write or paint. I was too excited by Doran's progress for regrets but disorganized material still bubbled up inside me. I suggested that words were only approximations; then I contradicted myself by demanding an exact and literal adherence to the principles of 'frequency', 'intensity', and 'duration'.

'Doran is charming,' I said. 'But this is closed brain surgery; it's a prolonged and terrible fight to save his life. We can only make it look easy as long as everyone understands.'

The next day we went creeping and walking at the country estate we'd been told had an adventure playground. The formal Elizabethan gardens with their rectangular fish ponds and fountains made a gracious background. The day was very peaceful; we worked our way steadily towards the playground which was the moment to switch over to creeping. At first sight the rope ladders and tree walks were obviously intended for well coordinated twelve-year-olds, not incoordinate infants. There was however a sandpit, a seesaw and a swing with a safety chair. I pointed these out to Doran; he crept disdainfully past them and on towards a rope bridge which climbed higher and higher between the trees and ended in a fort and a long slide. Since he crept well we decided to risk letting him have this dubious piece of vestibular experience. I held onto him so tightly I thought I was in danger of strangling him.

Doran was anxious to keep up with the other children and unaware of the discomforts of too vivid an imagination. When we reached the slide, perspiration was coursing through my fingers.

'That was good, wasn't it, Doran?' Antonia cried, bringing up the rear. I wished I could have seemed as calm. I was impatient to get down to earth again before she saw how needlessly overprotective I'd been.

'Wait,' I said. 'I'll go first, then I can catch you both at the bottom.'

I assumed he'd come down on Antonia's knee so I walked a little way off with my back to them to show I wasn't worrying, but I couldn't keep up the pretence. I turned round.

Antonia had put him on the slide sitting upright, like a normal child, and given him a push. Doran arched his spine lifted up into the air and fell head first towards me. I caught him in both arms and sank to my knees; the experience seemed to be recurring over and over again in slow motion.

'Antonia, I should have told you; Doran's still too stiff to sit, except in chairs.'

'That was horrible,' she said, touching his forehead to re-assure herself.

'But he's safe. If ever a child repelled the fact of death it's Doran.'

Doran was unhurt and untroubled. He wriggled down, crept to the direction of a line of huge drain pipes, and disappeared into them. There were various ways out, around which wand-ered the unfortunate parents whose offspring seemed to have determined to remain inside for good. I decided to follow Doran and promised if I saw anyone answering to the name of John or Richard I'd push them out too.

Alison wrote to Murray to explain her new situation.

'I'll ask him to come again,' she said. 'He was a help.' Then she said, 'Look, suppose you put an advertisement in the *New Scientist* for a volunteer. "Free board and lodging in superb English countryside in return for helping with an interesting new approach to brain injury." You need more help and at the moment I'm a liability.'

The advertisement went in and although I had a number of replies only one person actually arrived – fortunately exactly the right person. Carol was a graduate in Agriculture; she was tall, strong and to the point. She rolled up her sleeves and plunged in to do the washing up without being asked. She had no doubt that Doran was a formidable character with a strong will whom one could love without giving quarter. Although her background was about as far away as possible from Antonia's, their friendship grew to be one of the happiest. They devised and cooked new kinds of vegetarian recipes and took Lili on numerous outings in which she could play a princess. They became frequent clients of the local café which was one place in which things didn't turn to stone.

Bert appeared one afternoon.

'I've news for you, Linda.' I waited to be told the fund was in some inextricable state of crisis but she went on. 'We had a runner in the London Marathon. His name is Alf Smart. Jane Stimpson met him up at the club and he asked if he could run for Doran.'

'That's so kind.'

'He's raised over five hundred quid,' she said. 'You're very lucky again – pennies from heaven!'

As Doran's walking distances increased, rain also began to fall. The night after we'd dragged ourselves round Croydon Shopping Centre on a typically cold, drizzly day I dreamt of flat smooth floors and warm air. When I woke up I could put a name to the place. It was Gatwick airport. We collected our party and entered this apparent paradise of arrivals and departures, rich with trolleys, escalators and lifts. Doran acquired the chance to buy a plate of potato chips if he collected enough plastic ones. He soon knew every drinking fountain in the place. The cleaners adored him, pilots saluted him, the lady in the toy shop allowed him to carry toys out of one door of the shop and round to the cash desk at the other door. The barmaid always called him in for a glass of orange juice as soon as she saw him. If we went during the day we could go up to the observation platform and watch the planes take off. The sight of an aeroplane always kept Doran up for a few extra feet. The further he walked the less easy it was to catch him safely, and backing round Gatwick was extremely hazardous business. He could increase his speed very suddenly, particularly if he saw a downwards staircase ahead, or the way through passport control. He was even more successful at rushing into men's toilets, and getting him out of these masculine citadels demanded tact.

One day Carol came back from shopping with a set of reins.

'If you keep them dipped until the last moment so he can't hang on them, you'll save him getting rheumatism in his knees in later life.'

Doran liked the reins although he wasn't always happy to walk. As far as he was concerned walking had style but was useless for getting to the items one wanted, which were usually on the floor. He tried to change a few things beginning with the decision that it was inappropriate to be masked in a car. Having taxed him heavily I resorted to twisting his arms behind his back. Doran's next tactic was to slide forwards off my knee so that I was obliged to cross my legs over his and hold his head with my chin. Once the mask was over he resumed the sweetest disposition possible. Nevertheless he continued to assert himself. Getting him to walk when he wanted to creep was problematic. What did I do in a crowded street when Doran wouldn't move? I decided he could try buying his way out of sensory deprivation. This involved sitting on top of him with one's hands over his ears and eyes and a serene smile on one's face.

He could hold out for a long time. Sometimes he gave in gracefully and paid his chip; if not the seige persisted. It needed a certain loftiness of temperament to squat over a brain injured child in a public place. When Doran declined to surrender one had eventually to decamp. Unfortunately the moment he was picked up he acted as the winner of the round.

'You'll have to carry him a way that insults his dignity,' Carol suggested.

I tried various methods including upside down. Doran liked all of them until I hit upon hanging him over my shoulder by one foot. An elderly lady tapped me on the arm. 'I don't think your little boy's very comfortable,' she said.

Alison spent time in London collecting data for her trip. She came back with a pile of books and the idea of taking Doran to Brighton on his marathon day. Our object was to start early and be back in time to pick Lili up from school. We forgot the reins, but the weather cleared and when we reached the front the roundabouts had started up and people were beginning to buy ice creams. We heard a group of pensioners discussing him.

'Is that little boy normal?'

'He's just learning to walk.'

'He looks too old to be starting.'

'It depends on the child.'

'Perhaps he's been ill?'

Whatever it was, Doran did not present a straightforward picture of 'spasticity'.

As we reached the first fair he had enough chips to fly a fat aeroplane on the roundabout. Alison joined him; her vestibular was incredibly good. Doran went on walking jauntily along the promenade and it was easy to talk.

'When I feel like this it's worth all the pain and misery. The sea is so bright, Linda. Look at the streak of silver along the edge of the boat!'

'Are you a poet or a biologist?'

'I feel beauty so intensely I need to share it.'

'People really perceive things so differently! You see more and more of the one wave, but I'm already connecting it to the clouds in the sky.'

As Doran reached another landmark, Alison picked him up and raced down to the edge of the sea. By the time we reached the paddling pool he'd decided to walk through it. We turned onto the pier. Doran had covered nearly a mile without showing the slightest sign of fatigue. Every time he tottered towards the railings I raced in to shield him.

'What are you worried about?' Alison asked.

'I keep wondering if the water's deep enough for me to dive in and save him, or if I'd have to climb down the side for fear of smashing my head.'

She laughed. 'I've been looking for a life belt – so far I've not seen any.'

'Will I ever stop worrying about Doran?'

'At least you're only crazy about him. I'm crazy about everything.'

When I took Doran to the Ladies to change him, the attendant backed off him. I lingered to wash his hands.

'Don't let that child play with the water,' she shouted.

I saw she was under the impression brain injury was a

contagious disease. The day was too lovely to be anything other than understanding; I simply smiled and carried on.

Doran came home holding a windmill outside the car window. He had the greater glory of having walked nearly two miles with non-stop distances of up to ten metres.

Novelty remained his greatest motivation. Antonia decided to collect the addresses of people with large gardens and children who might welcome him as a friend. She went down the list. Most people seemed to be just going away or were away already. One woman who did not know me told Antonia that she was nonetheless a friend of a good friend of mine.

'That sounds hopeful,' I said.

'Wait a moment, this is really extraordinary. She then said that she was sure if she *did* meet you she couldn't stand you!'

'Did you ask her why, or who the friend was?'

'I most certainly did and she wouldn't say; she must be extremely theoretical.'

The next time Alison and I took Doran to Brighton it rained. Doran refused to walk, and Alison manifested all the symptoms of 'flu and collapsed by the paddling pool.

Murray came again on his way to Africa. His presence lightened Alison and made her feel less alone. We took Doran and Lili to Maidstone shopping centre and then to Alison's parents' house to creep.

Doran was in robust health; we were having lunch when he chewed heavily on a carrot and screamed in pain. I explored the interior of his mouth; there were dark cavities in his back teeth. There was no instant appointment at the dentist for a brain injured child. We had to wait for the next clinic which was in a school twenty miles away.

Alison dabbed the affected parts with a little ambersol out of a small bottle from the shelf and Doran soon demanded this treatment before every meal. He looked enormously grateful when he could finally climb into the dentist's chair, open his mouth and indicate the treatment he desired. The dentist was a locum who didn't want to drill without an anaesthetic. I refused the anaesthetic but Doran declined to leave the chair until something was done. The locum commenced apprehensively to dig, drill and finally fill the offending tooth. When it was finished Doran stood up and held out his hand.

'Ta,' he said politely.

'He said "thank you,"' I said.

'I know he did,' said the locum, sinking down into his own chair with relief. 'He was one of my best clients.'

The summer brought us an unusual round of garden parties, which could be translated into walking distances for Doran. He was now celebrated as a blue-eyed boy with a Charlie Chaplinesque gait. 'You don't have to pay for him.' 'That little one can have another go.' 'Would he like one of these?'

Doran wandered on as if the acquisition of this silver spoon were the most natural thing in the world. The kindness was real, enjoying it laid down more buffers against negativity. My understanding of the world depended greatly on my night's rest. Two aspects of Doran's early world remained part of his sleep pattern. He liked a dummy to suck and a bottle to drink. If he lost either of these props he fumbled about until he woke up and called out for them to be found.

Alison decided to abolish both at a stroke, and she bought him a rag doll, in exchange.

'Doran, you are approaching your fourth birthday. It is time you put away the things of a baby.'

Doran made a face, cleared his throat and gave way as if he'd been merely hanging on to an outdated custom. Within a week he'd forgotten them.

'Will you listen to me earlier next time?' she pleaded.

'If you promise not to bite your nails,' I said.

Doran grew increasingly confident. The day the car ran out of petrol at the top of the lane after we'd been to a Strawberry Fayre, he scrambled between the seats, and took the wheel while we pushed it home. Since he couldn't actually see the road I was obliged to help him with the steering. This did not

Doran with Joleen examining the arm on the coach to
0 Downing Street, December 1982.

At the House of Lords a child of courage celebrates with
Nerys Hughes and Derek Nimmo, December 1982.

September 1983. Skiing, good for balance.

reduce his sense of heroism and he continued driving an imaginary car for the rest of the evening.

Alison suffered from successive colds and tonsillitis, but a terrible disillusionment with the world and everyone in it seemed to predominate. Lili was very sympathetic to her moods and would often go upstairs to stroke her forehead.

'Mummy does get cross when you talk like that, but she doesn't really mean it. I think you should go down now and say you're sorry.'

When they found me it was always so peaceful and affectionate I wished I could do more for my friend.

Antonia asked tentatively if Alison was all right.

'She's meeting all the pain and the beauty in the world head on; the results are bound to be explosive.'

'I don't understand.'

'Don't worry, I do; but I can't help her directly. Concentrate on Doran. Where else can he walk?'

Alison knew a priory which was open to the public. Doran led us through cloisters, chambers and chapels. We brushed reverently past nuns and friars, taking care to keep Doran's reins dipped. Both children wanted to light a candle and kneel down. Lili thought heaven preferred to hear prayers aloud.

'And God bless Doran, and make him well.' Pause. 'And please make Alison kind to her feet.'

'What do you want, Alison?' I whispered.

'Peace of mind.'

'You don't mean tranquillity?'

'I think I'd be happier if there was a war.'

'Not for the killing?'

'For the excitement.'

'You'll have to turn to God, Alison; you're too good for the Devil. By the way have you noticed you're kneeling down.'

When Antonia left at the beginning of August, Carol came back to stay until we had a new CSV. Carol was a straightforward practical christian who acted rather than theorized. Although they were very different I realized Alison had the strength to admire her and this in itself created a change in the atmosphere. Doran saw Alison's frustration. He understood and forgave her as quickly as he exonerated himself. He was always staggering over to her holding out his hand. If Alison was angry with me he broke off whatever he was doing and flung himself between us.

'I think,' she said, 'the pain has finally settled across my back.'

Suzanne arrived; she was a very pretty twenty-two-year-old German who had joined CSV for a year's obligatory social work before she went to college. She insisted she knew all about aching backs. She persuaded Alison to lie on the floor and massaged her shoulders with a small tin of tiger balm.

'I do every night and you soon be well.'

'I think that will be enough.'

We looked hopefully at Alison's red skin.

'No, tomorrow, I do it. We persevere.'

Suzanne could teach Doran German. She was musical and had no difficulty helping me follow the metronome to do the respiratory patterning. She was strong, which meant she could help hoist Doran through his vestibular without giving way. It took a little while for me to recognize Suzanne was also afraid.

'The most important thing Doran needs is motivation,' I said, 'plus a calm well-organized atmosphere in which to work.'

'Good, I help. Where can I get driving lessons?'

'Driving lessons!'

'To help you I need to drive the car, yes?'

I didn't think there'd be time.

'Oh, I do and I should like to learn to ride and we will go to the seaside, Linda, yes!'

'Suzanne, this is not entirely a holiday.'

'But to work one must have time to oneself also.'

The next day we went to the shopping centre in Crawley. The Centre was a pedestrian precinct with a bandstand in the middle which attracted children. Doran followed them up the steps and marched round the railing. His laughter increased his rapport with them.

When Sue came back to visit he immediately flung himself to the floor and showed her his crawling. It was smooth and rhythmical; he reminded her of the long struggles she'd had with him and told her he'd come through.

'How are things?' she asked, putting her arm round me.

'Oh Sue! So far so good. Doran's well. I'm well. The future looks unstable, but the only way out is on.'

'Can I help?'

I laughed, 'If the going gets too tough, I'll call you.'

Suzanne mixed fruit, nuts and cereal for breakfast.

'Linda, you must teach me how to cook! What are you eating?'

'A poached egg.'

'I do not know this kind of egg? May I taste it? Yes, I think I am rather keen on poached egg. Will you cook me one?'

'I'll show you later; we have to pattern Doran.'

'First I wash.' She ran to the bathroom.

I felt that she washed her body to help drive the loneliness from her mind. She ate to give herself hope, the little bits she took from my plate seemed a plea for friendship. She wanted to sit down and just talk to me about anything and everything but this was not the point of my daily life. I began to despair of each new day. The practical necessity of my own sanity and Doran's wellbeing prompted me to call CSV. There was no one else immediately available. They suggested Suzanne needed more time. We had a fortnight before going back to America.

Bert turned up with a new idea for fund-raising to replace the sponsored crawl; it was a sponsored sunflower.

'I'm growing it by a neighbour's wall so there will be independent witnesses,' she said. 'People just have to sponsor it by the inch.'

I took a sheaf of forms and Doran and I handed them out round the shops in East Grinstead and Crawley. We were backed by the local newspapers. The idea of sponsoring a plant caught people's interest.

'If it grows too tall, it'll be an embarrassment,' she said. 'On the other hand if there's a storm I'm prepared to stand under an umbrella and hold it up.'

Suzanne decided to spend all her money on riding. She wrote to her friends as if no conflicts had occurred and often read the letters out to us.

'Suzanne,' I said, 'you never write of your own unhappiness.'

'Oh but that is mine. You are all so good to me here.'

'But you are living with us and you affect us. I don't want to hurt you.' Doran was a tower of emotional strength compared to Suzanne. She had tried to escape from herself by changing her situation and it hadn't worked.

'The way to change yourself is to throw your energy into helping someone else,' Alison said. 'I can see that; it has happened to me.'

'I try, you see. I'm afraid you don't like me unless I smile so I pretend to smile.'

'You don't need to be like that here,' Alison went on. 'Here at least we can be honest with each other.'

I listened to them hoping that the words spoken that night would still mean something by morning. We were taking Lili to Crawley to meet my mother and travel to the Island. It was Saturday and there would be a band on the square.

My mother met Doran in the playground; he flung himself on her rapturously. Lili wanted to take him with her. 'I'd do his programme, mummy,' she promised.

'You deserve a holiday, Lili; think of all that crawling.'

She did. 'All right, Doran, I'll send you a crab for the sandpit. Is my bucket and spade safe, grannie?'

It was and they left, holding hands and talking about my father and the health of the cats.

Suzanne and Alison went to do some shopping. While I steered Doran towards the square I could hear the sound of a band tuning up. When we turned the corner the music began. It was a West Indian Steel band. The shoppers were putting down their baskets gathering round the bandstand. I tucked Doran's reins up and let him go. The whole of Crawley seemed to have been brought to a standstill to listen except Doran who was kept up by the sheer vitality of the sound. His picture had been in the paper over the sunflower and people who recognized him called out, 'Don't stop, Doran! Bravo!'

Then a tall elderly woman, untidily dressed and rather the worse for drink stepped out.

'May I have the pleasure,' she said, and began to dance with him. Doran grinned.

'You are very welcome,' I said. 'Only you can't actually support him, he's got to balance himself.'

'If I can balance, he can too. Come on, young man, we'll show them.'

The woman had found her ideal partner. Doran danced, holding out his hands but not touching hers. He had been scheduled to walk for eighteen metres non-stop; he was now able to dance for at least eighty without a moment's support. When the music stopped the woman melted away. I could see Alison and Suzanne coming back through the crowds.

16

---❋---

Doran walked down Broadway. We stayed overnight at Judith's brother's; he was a psychotherapist who kept his flat full of large stuffed animals. From the window we could look out across the river.

Judith wanted to celebrate. 'Let's take the Statten Island ferry,' she said. 'And incidentally, I think it's a wonderful idea, but Americans as a rule don't understand reins.'

On the way out a boy of about ten came up on roller skates. 'What you got him tied up for?' he called out.

'He doesn't think he's manacled to his mother. He's English. He thinks he's a horse,' I said.

Doran liked American money. He bought our tickets for the ferry and a large bag of popcorn for himself. As the boat drew out a young couple wearing old-fashioned clothes and carrying full champagne glasses leant against the rail. The gulls swooped in to be fed popcorn but the bride and groom held hands and stared into the middle distance.

'Dreaming is free for some,' said Judith, 'but you and Doran can't afford it.'

At the Institutes Doran was an acknowledged walking victory. The staff continued to marvel at his undamaged knees, so eventually we felt brave enough to produce the reins. I could see Rosalind thought them undignified and un-American.

'Nevertheless,' she said, 'they evidently worked and I think I might recommend them to other families.'

We went through the report.

'What do you think is Doran's biggest problem?'

'Everything is affected by his breathing.'

'What would you do about it?'

'I'd increase his crawling to help reorganize his brain, and the respiratory patterning to give him more regular breathing.'

'Full marks. Let's take a look at your crawling, Doran.'

Doran crawled as if it were his greatest joy, unaware he was letting himself in for four hundred yards of it a day. His balance was good enough to eliminate the passive vestibular programme and replace it with walking up and down hill, walking on rough terrain, and walking on the flat. We needed only to turn out of our cottage to the left to find a slope and to the right to find a long flat stretch of road, while behind us lay the fields. Doran had to do ten metres, ten times a day of spring creeping, and brachiation. Brachiation meant swinging from an overhead ladder which would improve his chest size and therefore his respiration. He had four cross-patternings and four half hour respiratory patternings a day, a language programme, masking and intelligence.

On the way back to the airport, Judith decided it was time to introduce our star to his former benefactor, her father. 'I think Doran is finally acceptable to Long Island society,' she said.

'Judith, this is the greatest compliment you've paid him so far.'

It involved certain safeguards. When we got into the elegant dining room Doran's end of the table had been tactfully swathed in polythene. He ate like a prince.

Alison collected us at Heathrow. We spent an hour waiting to get out of the car park so, to revive our spirits, she stopped at the pub in the village. We sat in the garden. Doran kept getting up to pick the huge blackberries he could now recognize in the hedge. A man at the next table leant forward.

'I once wrote an article on him for the *Courier*. I can hardly believe it.'

'He does have some way to go yet,' I said, thinking about the four hundred yards crawling.

When we turned out of the village towards home, Doran's

face dropped; by the time the car stopped at the gate he was howling. Suzanne ran anxiously down the path assuming he'd broken a leg.

'No, it's okay,' I said, 'the reality has struck him; six more months of hard work to pay for his week of glory.'

Gradually he realized he was having a day's respite.

Alison flung open the toy box. 'Doran it's all yours for the afternoon – make the most of it.' He climbed in head first.

Peter promised to come the next day and build our brachiation ladder. 'It's a bit backward isn't it, turning him into a monkey?' he said. When we tried Doran's walking the question of measurement arose.

'Let's paint the road,' I suggested. 'I have a large tin of yellow paint.'

We proceeded solemnly. I held the pot, Alison paced out the metres, dipped in the brush and wrote them down as if she were from the water board. Doran could now see his goals clearly ahead of him; when he reached them he could pick himself a few handfuls of blackberries.

Two days after we'd undertaken this act of vandalism on the road the Crawley police phoned up. 'Are you the lady with the handicapped little boy?'

'Yes.'

'The one who goes to America?'

'Yes.'

'Good. Well, we're having an open day at the leisure centre and we'd like to raise some money for him.'

'What! I mean that's wonderful. Thank you. Thank you very much.'

Another aspect of the new programme which was to Doran's advantage was his ability to earn two hours off it every week. He decided what he wanted most was to join the play school as a normal child; since this was not in fact the case one of us went with him to see that as far as possible he behaved like one. His height and general appearance compared favourably with his comrades and as no one was particularly verbal his lack of speech was hardly obvious. The small boy he admired most spent a lot of the time standing in the corner with his hands behind him.

Lili was the only person I knew who had the measure of her brother. I phoned my mother to ask what time she was coming home. It seemed Lili had grown very attached to the school on the Isle of Wight; her reading and writing were developing in leaps and bounds. Could she stay on until half term? Both my parents and Lili herself were very eager to settle the matter.

'Don't forget to write often,' I said.

'Mummy, I'm sending Doran a crab.'

It arrived in sea water with instructions from my mother on building an aquarium.

The walks up and down hill began to seem less attractive when the blackberries had fallen and the wind and rain blew into one's face. It was also impossible to detect cars when Doran was complaining. We were often forced into the hedge and came back covered in mud and grit, wondering how we'd ever get through another day. I had put the winter out of my mind when I first posted up the programme. The rough terrain was true to its name, the fields were now churned up by cows and horses and full of large boggy pools. A few steps was the best Doran could manage before he fell flat on his face. He had further decided that although he could crawl, it was difficult and took a long time; he had almost convinced us that dead slow and stop were the only paces possible. Sprint creeping went rather better mainly because Doran knew it would be over quickly. He missed having Lili to look forward to when she came bursting in from school; since I had no friends with children his age, he felt frustrated for companionship. The programme had become an anticlimax; he could walk but he still wasn't free.

Although we lost time I decided to take him into East Grinstead to do his hour walking on the flat. We discovered a few slopes in the town which were more fun than our lane. These had to be paced out since I was reluctant to try yellow paint in front of the traffic wardens. Woolworths' attracted Doran off the street – he made a beeline for a space gun which produced an appallingly loud noise, accompanied by flashing lights – and rushed off. I followed, intent upon catching up with him before he collided with the glass lampshades on the next counter. He went on walking; he circled the ground floor of the store and put the gun back where he'd found it. Then he picked up a cowboy hat, rammed it on his head and started off again.

On marathon days we usually played safe and went to Gatwick; besides the airport there was also the Gatwick Hilton. Alison and I wandered in as casually as two people can with a brain injured child on a short rein. We were absorbed into a labyrinth of carpeted corridors with lines of doors on which exhausted passengers had hung plastic 'Do not Disturb' notices.

Doran carefully removed the reins from my hands and held them himself. This seemed admirable until we saw that his intention was to rattle as many of the door handles as he could in the hope of being invited inside for a late breakfast. After a fight, we disengaged him and sped down to the next floor before we could be caught. Doran was still holding a 'Do not Disturb' notice, we left it on another door as we went out.

Alison was counting off the weeks before she left. She had been keeping a bottom drawer of useful things to take to French Guiana. It now included a tin mug and plate, an expensive pink bath towel and a collection of novels for reading in the forest.

'Won't it be rather heavy?' I ventured.

'It'll be better than using leaves,' she said.

Suzanne decided she would leave in November to go back to Germany and study singing. I needed two people to help on a continuous basis so we tried advertisements in *New Scientist* and *Time Out*.

There were numerous phone calls but it was impossible to tell what the applicants were like. Brian, an ex-social worker who looked a bit like Woody Allen but was taller, arrived from Scotland. He stayed the weekend, accompanied us on Doran's marathon walk round town and country and showed every sign

266

of dedicated involvement. After borrowing five pounds plus a packet of cigarettes from Alison, he promised to come back on Thursday to start work. Brian rang to confirm everything so we sat back and waited. By the following weekend there was still no sign of him; we were regretfully forced to give him up for dead.

The next applicant was a girl with a pretty black kitten who drank black coffee and refused all offers of food. As the days went by I became afraid that I might be in some way responsible and wondered what nutrition I could possibly slip unnoticed into coffee. Her refuge was the bible, but it didn't take away her aura of perpetual night. After a week she conceded Doran's necessity to have light and life around him, thanked me for allowing her to stay, took the kitten and left.

An ex-psychology student came down next, followed by a theology graduate. They asked a great many questions before retiring to the station, and the security of their normal lives.

I had several calls from an Ian, who seemed to be in a different part of the country on each occasion and unlikely ever to reach us. Then he contacted me to say he expected to be at East Grinstead station in a matter of hours. In desperation I agreed to give him a try. Doran walked down the street to the station. The autumn leaves were piling up everywhere and he kicked through them into the waiting room. There was a very tall man, who looked thirtyish, reading a cycling magazine.

Doran rushed over to him, flinging his arms round his knees. The man smiled. 'You must be Doran,' he said. 'Hello, how are you then?' Doran remained entwined round Ian; it was love at first sight.

Later that evening a knock at the door revealed a young woman under an enormous back-pack. 'Hello,' she said, 'I found you! I'm Lily.' I dimly remembered having spoken to someone called Lily but had entirely forgotten when I'd invited her down. Nevertheless she had arrived and I liked the look of her.

Lily was a South African physiotherapist in her early

twenties who was hitchhiking round Europe. Ian turned out to be forty; he had spent most of his life travelling on a bicycle and had learnt to live with the greatest economy. 'People,' he said, 'are stupid. If they got together to help each other there'd be no problems but they choose to go after money and then they complain.'

The philosophy of the programme was of no interest to him beyond the fact that it was good for Doran. This was enough, because if Ian was with us Doran wanted to succeed.

The next day was November the fifth. Doran crawled to the accompaniment of a box of indoor fireworks, obligingly moving a few feet for a flare and a few more feet for a mine of snakes. The evening was illuminating, but for crawling to be effective it should be done on a non-stop basis.

That night we argued the matter at the table while Lily fried some dough to make a bread which she said one ate round the camp fire on the Veldts. The upshot was no more toys, games or books. Doran must crawl at least one round of the house without stopping.

'Can he make that?' Lily asked.

'Doran could crawl a thousand feet a day before he could do anything else,' I said. 'The block is purely tactical.'

Suzanne left the next day. Alison put her on the train. 'She was brave,' she remarked. 'I feel suddenly sad, do you?'

'The world seems very small to me. When the situation is right people meet again.'

'This year, next year, sometime? – never?'

'In another incarnation, my dear!'

Doran was given a clear course and the new laws about crawling. Loud complaints, jokes or trying to creep away meant being sat on and masked. There was no lunch until he cooperated.

'Doran, are you staying there, or are you crawling and joining us for the meal?'

Doran's hunger got the better of him. He crawled furiously round the house, pulled himself up and walked over to his chair.

'I don't believe my eyes,' Ian exclaimed. 'Two chips please, Doran,' I requested. 'The game's up, you can't pretend it's not possible to crawl fast.'

Doran ate his rice thoughtfully.

After a week of this Alison pointed out that Doran was walking better. 'Yes,' I said, 'it's the crawling. It means that improved breathing and increased neurological reorganization reflects on all levels of function.'

'That seemed a reasonably scientific observation,' she said, 'but without a parallel universe it's impossible to be sure.'

Lily got a job as a physio in Brighton and Ian was offered an interview at a hostel in London to supervise ex-psychiatric patients. The most sensible thing to do was return to the support of CSV. I was promised help as soon as possible, and although Lily left, Ian offered to stay on until we were secure.

Lili came home at half term; she was delighted with Ian. I realized he talked non-stop to children whereas Alison and I had to prise conversation out of him. One day I asked, 'Don't you talk to people over ten years old?'

'That's about the time people start to get stupid.'

Lili dug out all her dolls and teddy bears to be Doran's audience.

'Mummy,' she said, 'grannie wants me to stay at my new school.'

'Do you like it?'

'Yes, I like my teacher.'

'Would you like to go back there until Christmas?'

She nodded.

'You do write beautiful letters, Lili.'

'Can Doran write yet?'

'No.'

'When I come back I'll teach him.'

There was no play school at half term, so I took them both to the cinema. We had to queue pressed together along a steep carpeted slope. The children began to slip away from their parents and run up and down; waiting was tedious although it was at least inside, out of the rain. The result was that the following morning Ian and I were in the same cinema poised at opposite ends of the slope while Doran ferried bits of jigsaw puzzle between us.

The day before Lili went back to my parents we had a marathon day at Gatwick. Lili tucked Doran's reins up so that he could escape; Ian initiated a spontaneous musical comedy. By the time we lined up on the moving pavement Doran had nearly made his interim report goal. Then Ian decided to round off the evening by sending his clogs along separately, while Doran leant on the hand rail bursting with laughter.

Two young police officers, unused to innocent high spirits, approached.

'What do you think you're doing?' the first policeman began.

'Put your shoes on,' the other advised.

Ian didn't move.

'Shame,' Alison called out, 'he was only amusing the child.' (Since Ian was taller than either constable they could hardly be told to pick on someone their own size.)

'Do you live near here?' the first policeman went on.

'You have no right to intimidate this man,' Alison continued.

I turned to the policeman. 'The gentleman you have just spoken to so rudely has had a hard day working with a brain injured child in whom your Chief Constable has taken a very keen interest. In future will you kindly wait before you criticize. I assume you are both at a loose end after a rather dull day.'

Their mouths dropped open and by the time the pavement had successfully shifted us to the car park the matter was resolved without a breach of the peace. Doran beamed benignly from his superior position on Ian's shoulders.

From now on every time the phone rang I flew to it in case it was CSV. I knew Ian wanted to move to London. Each day he stayed was a present to us but it couldn't last indefinitely; he had to take the job.

One afternoon I picked up the receiver to find *Woman's Own* at the end of the line. 'We wanted to let you know that Doran has been nominated as one of our "Children of Courage".

There's a very strong chance that this will be confirmed quite soon.'

'Yes,' I said. 'Thank you' – and put the receiver down without the least idea of what it meant.

For the next two weeks whenever the telephone rang it seemed to be *Woman's Own*. What's Doran's age exactly? What was the name of the clinic in America? Could I send them a recent photo?

When at last the call was from CSV I had to remember to sound appropriately urgent. Nevertheless they had found a young man of seventeen, Cain, and a twenty-year-old German girl whose name was Elvira.

Ian left the day Elvira came. We took her to Woolworth's on the way home and I tried to explain the whole thesis of the programme without inhibiting Doran's walking style.

Elvira spoke very little but she made sure everything she said made sense. When she had a phone call from Germany passionate voluble German prose poured from her lips. 'So that's really you,' I said.

'It's horrible to have no words when I really want to speak.'

In the meantime she taught Doran German and Russian. His Russian pronunciation sounded nearer the mark than his English; Elvira's greatest worry was that she wasn't doing enough.

Cain appeared a week later. We had difficulty persuading him to put Doran down.

'I love babies,' he said.

'Doran isn't a baby, physically or mentally, and he's tough, tough, tough,' I said.

The more Cain realized what Doran's daily life entailed, the more horrified he looked.

'Come on now, loving a child isn't enough; you have to respect it. Respecting Doran is making him do his programme,' I told him.

Cain ruffled Doran's hair and looked dubious. He was up early next morning. When we came down he was in the bathroom. He was still in the bathroom an hour later. By this time Alison was desperate enough to pee in the garden. We eventually got him out.

'Speed is the essence,' I said.

By the end of the month Doran was no longer the apple of Cain's eye; he had become the stone in the pond. On the other hand Doran was crawling as though forty yards were as easy as four yards had been the month before. Elvira read to him while he ate.

'Don't you think he gets too much attention?' Cain asked Alison.

'That depends on how much attention I think I'm getting,' she joked. 'Would you like to be Doran?'

I opened my mail.

'Listen, this is from *Woman's Own*. Doran has been chosen as a child of courage; that means we go up to London and receive an award from the Queen Mother.'

'What sort of award?' Cain asked.

'They don't say.' I read on, 'We have two nights at a hotel and dinner at the House of Lords with well-known celebrities and. . . .'

'And,' said Alison.

'And since I told them that if we were invited anywhere the programme had to go on, they said I could have you to help me!'

Alison hugged me.

'Come on now,' I said, 'it'll be hard work.'

'Doran will love it!'

Doran had stopped eating and begun to listen.

'Doran,' I said, 'heroes still have to crawl; it's an ongoing thing.'

Cain managed to reduce his time in the bathroom but we had difficulty in dragging him from in front of the mirror.

'Do you think I look better with a fringe?' he said.

'You're very handsome, Cain; I'd avoid gilding the lily. Can you pick up the stop watch, we're leaving for East Grinstead.'

'Wait a minute. If I get my camera will someone take a picture of me?'

Elvira sighed. 'Cain, you never pick Doran up without doing your hair first.'

'Doran doesn't need people to wait on him.'

'He can't get up by himself,' she said.

'You should make him try.'

'Cain,' I said, 'your motive may be mean, but actually you're right!'

Remembering when not to help Doran was becoming more difficult. He could affect a limp with such pathos he might have got into drama school on the strength of it. He had a fine memory of every bump and scratch including the places along the road where he'd received them. I stopped picking him up and let him reach out for my hand. Every time he indicated he could do something for himself once, we awarded him with the opportunity of doing it all the time. He returned the compliment with comic limitations; if anyone transgressed in their table manners they could see themselves at once opposite reflected in the blue-eyed mirror.

A few days before we were due to go to London a television team arrived. This time Doran wasn't filmed lying face downwards on the table; he was walking along the road in front of the cameras. It was impossible to believe the same trip had once bored him to unyielding rage. He caught up with the microphone and made to make a long interesting statement in what appeared to be Ancient Celtic.

'He still has trouble because he tries to say everything in one breath. When his respiration is better he'll give you his own story rather more clearly,' I said.

'The clinic you go to is still controversial, isn't it?' they asked.

'They may not know all the reasons why their programmes work. If that were true the world would understand a great deal more about the brain than it does. There's no end to their research; meanwhile they don't leave children to drown when they know they can pull them out of the water.'

The day we went to London was one of the coldest of the

year. We were given a taxi to take us to Crawley station and on closer scrutiny, the tickets turned out to be first class. Doran settled down in his unusually comfortable seat and crossed his legs like Alison.

'Does he have to do all his programme?' she asked.

'He's here because of his programme so, besides the fact that he needs to do it, it's a great opportunity to show it off.'

'But all the time?'

'It's quite obvious that whatever we try to do it won't be a hundred percent, but if we don't try to do a hundred percent the results will be worse.'

'You mean you won't mask him when he's shaking hands with the Queen Mother?'

'Probably not.'

Alison paused for a moment then she said, 'Didn't you once have Doran's astral chart given to you? This seems like an event that should have been mentioned.'

'I remember that Doran had Jupiter rising.'

'What does that mean?'

'It means he has a lucky star. He may ride dangerously but fortune should save him at the eleventh hour.'

'Fortune seems to have cut it a bit fine if his past is anything to go by.'

'Well, here we are balanced on Doran's star. Heaven sent this for pure pleasure, to revive the soul. A first class apartment is blissful.'

'I thought it contradicted all you believe.'

I stretched out my feet. 'Alison, I acknowledge magic.'

When the taxi turned into St Ermine's Hotel and we saw the elaborate Victorian façade with its sparkling glass doors, behind which glimmered a huge Christmas tree, Alison succumbed.

'This is beyond anything I imagined!'

We'd both privately felt the hotel would be a second class, very solid, child-proof affair. We were shown to a large room with three single beds, a bathroom and a television. We dragged Doran away from these delights and went into the lounge where a group of mothers and children drinking tea suggested we might have found the rest of the team. Having tried out a chair and been masked, Doran wanted to explore the hotel. I looked round hopefully for someone of his own age. These were the most modest unassuming collection of heroes and heroines you could imagine. Doran seemed alone in his immodest exuberance.

A man came round with a tray of chocolates; since old habits die hard I intervened, 'Doran doesn't eat them; he's on a strictly whole-food diet.' A small girl appeared from behind my back and handed him her piece while she retrieved another from the tray.

'My name is Joleen. Do you want to see my arm?' she asked. Doran sat down attentively, sucking his chocolate.

'Mummy, can I have my arm?'

The arm, which I now realized was not part of the body corporate of the small girl, was passed over. It was a battery operated limb which she could move by thinking. Doran admired it and tried it on.

'Can't he talk properly?' she asked. 'What's wrong with him?'

I explained about Doran's injury and his physical programme.

'I can do somersaults,' she said. 'Would you like to go for a walk?'

Doran indicated that he certainly would like to go for a walk and especially with her. She took his reins and he led the way round the hotel. Alison and I followed them, just fast enough to prevent their escape through the revolving doors.

When we were collectively introduced to the dining room there was a buffet laden with every different kind of meat, salad and cheese. Doran insisted that his plate looked like Alison's which meant helping him to sausage and turkey. Having turned the meat over a few times his vegetarian background prevailed; he abandoned it in favour of camembert, alongside a plate of fruit salad voluptuously crowned with cream. By this time the children were all wearing huge badges proclaiming their identity and the words *Woman's Own* Child of Courage'.

The schedule involved rising quite early to be taken by coach to Westminster Abbey for interviews with the press and television in the Jerusalem Chamber. Then came the presentation of the awards by the Queen Mother and our informal meeting with her. We were going to walk across the road to the House of Lords for lunch, but between lunch and the celebration dinner the events were still mysterious.

An early night was desirable, so Doran was reluctantly parted from his clothes and his badge. Although we could put him to bed we couldn't make him sleep. He had two baths, about twenty-two flushes of the toilet and the benefit of the television. We pushed the beds together so that he felt he was missing nothing. At about eleven o'clock when an 'Arts Review' appeared he went to sleep. Nevertheless we were first down for breakfast, with Doran bright-eyed, fresh, and looking for Joleen.

Doran's lack of coherent speech should have made him an unlikely candidate for an interview, but the spectacle of Doran and Joleen in tandem circuiting the chamber falling into cameras right and left, was too good for the press to miss. He was outrageously happy although his appearance was deteriorating fast, so after an initial battle to retrieve some standards, I gave priority to the pleasure of the moment.

Once in the Abbey a peace descended while we listened to the carols. Doran clapped after each one and clapped still more for the Queen Mother. One by one each child went up to collect a cube of perspex with a small gold bird flying through it, and a large certificate. Getting back without dropping the cube on the Queen Mother's foot, or irredeemably screwing up the certificate, demanded the skills of a conjuror, if Doran were apparently to be free enough to have any hand in the matter. On the way back to the Jerusalem Chamber I lost sight of both children in the rush. Fortunately Alison was ahead; by the time I reached her Doran had already collided with the Queen Mother.

'What did you do, Alison,' I cried.

'She asked me if he'd like some orange juice.'

'What did you say?'

'I said yes, I thought so, and then she poured him a glass, and I think she said he was doing very well. Where is he now?'

Doran was heading off towards the Dean of Westminster with a precariously full cup of orange.

Alison caught my arm, 'Do you realize this room's full of celebrities?'

'No.'

'Can't you recognize them?'

'Alison, I haven't had a television for twenty years.'

'It's amazing. Here you are with Doran surrounded by famous people and you might as well be in the bus station waiting room for all they mean to either of you.'

'Doran has sixth sense; this is rather more than the bus station, Alison!'

After about half an hour there was a sense of a new organization taking place by the door and we all trooped back to the Abbey to be photographed with the Queen Mother. The small children were asked to stand in front of her and the older ones at the sides. I knew Doran had to keep moving to hold his balance. If Joleen were left to hold him the result would be that two children, ultimately perhaps the whole group, would soon be running round in circles. The only thing left for me was to kneel at the Queen Mother's feet, hold on to Doran's trousers and hide behind him without giving the impression that his real disability was the possession of an extra pair of hands.

At last we made a long crocodile across the road for lunch. The House of Lords dining room was piled high with delicacies. Joleen seemed to be feeding Doran Quality Street and Smarties, but I pretended not to notice. In the middle of lunch there was an announcement that Mrs Thatcher had found time to give us a tour of 10 Downing Street. Alison decided to waste no time taking the photographs. She picked up Doran, complete with party hat and teaser.

'I shall commemorate this day with a picture of him sitting on celebrated laps. He can find out who they were later,' she said. Doran looked like the proverbial old friend who arrives at the wedding reception straight from the stag party; he was eating from several different dishes at once, and drinking Coca-Cola. I had to use the opportunity to discuss the plight of thousands of less well blessed brain injured children who languished in untold numbers in institutions before Doran undermined my case by collapsing beneath the table. He was in fact made of sterner stuff; once we gathered back into the coach to proceed to 10 Downing Street he was able to angle for a seat next to Joleen and finish the chocolates.

'Mummy,' she said, 'it's very hot. May I take my arm off?' for a seat next to Joleen and finish the chocolates.

The arm was detached and the two of them reviewed its mechanism with scientific interest until we reached Downing Street. When he was set on his feet again Doran's late night, early morning and all that he had celebrated in between showed in his sudden absence of legs. Jolyen held his collar. It was with the affectionate smile of a diminutive Falstaff that Doran allowed himself to be guided up the steps of Number 10. Mrs Thatcher was quick to realize that the safest thing to do with Doran was to pick him up. Accordingly the cameras flashed. Now the burden of verticality had been unexpectedly removed, he lolled gratefully against her shoulder in a semi-stupor. In this way he was immortalized with an unlikely companion.

After a tour of the lights and supper, which in Doran's case was mostly chips and pulling crackers, he staggered into an armchair by Jolyeen and fell asleep.

The next morning a picture of Doran with his mouth open and his eyes turned heavenward in the arms of his country's leader appeared across the front page of *The Times* and the *Telegraph*. The more revived version of the same boy was nonetheless impressed. On the way home we shared our first class compartment with the line of businessmen buried in open papers.

'Dor, Dor, Dor,' Doran pointed out.

One by one they turned their papers round to see what Doran was looking at.

'He's the brain injured child of the future,' I said. 'He's not just regaining his potential, he's revaluing it.'

Doran pointed to his badge. The businessmen smiled shyly and retreated to their editorials.

'Are you drunk?' Alison asked me.

'This is still heady stuff. Think of those hours on our hands and knees round the ladder.'

'And sitting on Doran's back in Tunbridge Wells.'

'Now he's walking further and further every day. He can afford to carry all the other hurt children with him.'

'You see him leading them over the barricades to the Institutes?'

'Why not? I'm a romantic fool, remember?'

'Will you feel like that when Doran does his crawling in the morning?'

We laughed. On the way home I paid a rare visit to the village shop to collect some groceries. As I turned to leave, a woman whose husband had helped pattern stopped me. 'Congratulations, I saw Doran on the television. You've proved us all wrong.'

In a few days Lili came home. Doran's rough terrain was now quite impressive and she wanted Alison and I to watch her take him walking across the fields. The air was fresh and cold, the large pools over the grass were covered with ice which cracked like toffee underfoot. Doran climbed a frozen molehill, stepped down steadily and stamped towards the next one.

'Is Doran well now, mummy?' Lili asked.

'He's in good shape; but as you can see, we're still working.'

'I think he's better,' she said. Then she grabbed his hand and made off in the direction of the village.

'Hey, wait a minute,' Alison called. 'Where are you going?'

'Doran and me are going to school.'

'Is that your last word?' I asked.

'Yes, mummy. Come on, Doran!'

POSTSCRIPT

THE FULL POTENTIAL of any human being is a matter for speculation. Different cultures make a variety of demands on the young, encouraging and discouraging different abilities. Doran has responded to the opportunity offered by the accumulative effects of his programme. It is only familiarity with the observable stages of human development that makes us believe that a tiny baby will one day get up and walk. No one looking at such a child for the first time without these references could believe it would happen. In the same way it is only through familiarity with brain injured children on the programme that one can predict the apparently impossible will happen. At eighteen months Doran's underdeveloped puppet-like body gave no indication of any potential for movement. There was no way that his frame as it then existed could support its own weight. There was no reason to assume he would ever stand or walk.

Day after day Doran walked his metres of rough terrain in bleak fields, the wind invariably against him, cutting into his face. We longed for the time when he could stand upright unaided and so avoid the continual battering of his knees as he fell over between furrows of frosty soil. Sarah Neal replaced Cain. She was eighteen years old, but had an extraordinary internal strength. She was also very methodical. I was no longer in danger of forgetting my records. Doran kept struggling near to his goal, but the bad weather constantly frustrated us and our visit was postponed until March. There was no way we could complete the distance in the daylight, so eventually Elvira and I took him to the rough side of the Hartfield recreation ground with torches and a bar of chocolate as a final inducement. He kept going while we sang, joked or implored, until he accepted a challenge beyond his normal threshold. He was still walking at 8 p.m. At 8.15 we celebrated with coffee, warm milk and crisps outside the local pub. The barman brought these drinks out into the cool February night without comment.

It continued to freeze and Doran's falls grew more worrying. At last he appeared to have strained a muscle in his leg and developed a realistic enough limp to impress me that it was time to stop. The best alternative was to give him long hours of respiratory patterning.

Doran was relieved and cooperative. After a few days of this we were all aware that his range of sounds was wider, that his convergence seemed better and that he fed himself with a far greater proficiency.

His leg was showing positive signs of recovery by the time Alison left for French Guiana. He tried to hobble to the door with her, waving goodbye to the rest of us, and holding tightly on to her hand. She proposed to be away for at least two years.

A week later when we were sitting opposite Rosalind I half-jokingly suggested putting Doran on a respirator.

'Mrs Scotson, I have been considering just that. Would you like to volunteer?'

Doran's unresolved problems lay with his irregular respiration. It was impossible for him to breathe and carry on another purposeful activity such as talking and taking steps. We had to wait until September for the respirator to become available. Meanwhile his new programme increased the manual respiratory patterning to four hours a day for five weeks, and two marathon days of six hours. His goals were to crawl for thirty minutes a day reaching four hundred metres in less than twenty-two minutes, to walk non-stop on the flat without falling over for twenty minutes, to walk a mile on rough terrain in forty-five minutes and to brachiate four independent rungs of his ladder. He also acquired skis and ski boots to help his balance, he was to walk two hundred metres with skis in under thirty minutes and to stand for five minutes in his boots. I returned in high spirits, our future prospects had never looked so high. One critical problem remained. We had no money left in the fund and we were in debt to the Institutes. Family matters prevented Bert from carrying on the committee; it was left to Judy Blowe and I somehow to change our fortunes.

Local people had given all they could; I could put no further demands on them. Then I reflected that Doran was not only a local figure, he was already a symbol of hope to many families. He could be sponsored to do his own programme, to walk a mile in less than an hour. I phoned the papers and wrote to the celebrities we met at Westminster. Judy began the organization. Before we had gone very far the *Sunday People* stepped 'n to help. Then two prisoners, from Lewes Jail, made soft toys for us to raffle, while others ran an amazing half marathon. We found unknown benefactors, and in one summer the financial anxiety which had pursued us was swept away.

Doran had an idyllic summer. The pastures were now covered in buttercups, the grass was warm and he could earn a swim in the stream. When we took him skiing on the recreation ground the local boys wanted to swap their bikes for his skis.

One evening I was still writing intelligence cards close to midnight when a dark figure appeared at the back door. I decided that if this were not a friend then it would be better if it became one very quickly. I was too tired to cope with an enemy. So, I said 'hello' as cordially as possible in its direction. Alison emerged from the shadows and collapsed in a chair. She was very brown, shaken and swollen with insect bites. After some weeks of anguish she encountered a practitioner of Chinese acupuncture and determined that her own vocation lay in healing. She was accepted at the College of Oriental Medicine. Since then her life has become steadily more harmonious while her bracing consciousness continues to revive me.

We returned to the Institutes and Doran got his respirator. When Anne Ball fixed him into it and switched it on his face was wreathed in smiles. For the first time he was relieved of a continuous fight for breath. His programme was to be eight hours on the machine, reducing slowly to four hours over the next six months. His main physical goal was to walk fifty metres in one hour on skis. Judith suggested we put a commercial greenhouse in the garden which was not a joke but a realistic idea. Doran would have preferred snow.

We put Doran on the sawn-off top of the patterning table with the respirator, which was a converted Hoover vacuum cleaner, on the floor beside him. A tube attached to a jacket over his chest and sucked air out of it to a regular beat, which was adjusted on the control panel. The machine sounded like an amplified heart beat but we learned not to hear it. The results were impressive. When it broke down the local Hoover dealer came to our rescue and a spare part was flown over from America. Doran slept better; he didn't wake up in the morning stiff and uncomfortable; he could stand in his own shoes for as long as he liked. He walked his fifty metres in the greenhouse and began to use a few clear words appropriately, including the word 'no', with a distinctly upper class inflection. He began to insist on using the toilet himself and within a week he had exchanged his nappies for underpants. He learned to walk safely up and down stairs which allowed him the privilege of a room of his own. Doran basked in his independence. If he woke early he preferred to snuggle back with a book than to wake me. After five years I was reintroduced to a continuous night's sleep. We had a series of superb volunteers – Neil, Jan, Daphne, Simon, Amanda and Dave. Each one saw Doran through new, vital stages in his development.

He is now doing a hundred independent somersaults a day and running twenty fifty-metre sprints in each two miles of walking at about twenty-five seconds on average. He can read aloud from books and is beginning to write and spell. He is still using the respirator, the results are both positive and liberating. In many ways Doran's abilities are above rather than below average for his age. We still need to improve his coordination and balance, and to improve his speech; but the pathways have been forged, they simply need reinforcement.

Further development towards the actual realization of his potential seems within his grasp. Once no one looking at him could imagine how such a child would make these tremendous goals; now people say, 'Yes, with Doran that's realistic. What's he going to do next?'

Did I ever believe I would fail? The honest answer is no, because the only failure I understood was indifference. Although I made light of it at the time I knew the journey would be long and difficult, but at every turn we were discovering things about Doran which were exciting and illuminating – besides which Doran was patently enjoying himself; life began to fulfil his expectations. Our desperation left us; both children were infused with a sense of purpose which strengthened them. Their mutual respect delighted us. A new admiration and friendship between myself and my parents blossomed and became substantial. Beyond this what we were discovering added to the sum of the information the Institutes had to help other children. Life is for learning, whatever the apparent misadventure; it offers a new route into the depth of human love and human philosophy. No action is so small or insignificant not to have a positive or a negative effect on the whole. Many people united to help Doran and to each I owe my thanks. What they did lives in him and in the children who will find their way to a new future through the Institutes' work.

I was never given more than it was possible for me to undertake, and I have met enough courageous people to feel a sweet humility. From childhood I longed to serve some ideal in a very practical way. The degree of specialization in our culture made me an outsider longing to combine art with science and intuition with analysis.

What has happened to Doran need not be exceptional. We will never know enough about the brain but we can see when a treatment principle wins results. Einstein once pointed out that he could not hope to acquire knowledge but only to increase the boundaries of his understanding. There is a grave need; a facility has arisen to meet it. On humanitarian grounds alone this should not be denied.

POST POSTSCRIPT

WHILE I WAS writing the postscript, Doran's development seemed to be exceeding the pace of my longhand. He grabbed a piece of paper and wrote the word 'Go', illustrating it with a set of traffic lights.

'Red, Orange, Go!' he declared. (This is a record of the lights he passes on the way to the local recreation ground to do his running). He began to introduce couplets into his conversation: 'yellow bag', 'big apple', 'blue car'. If asked the question 'What does a plant need to grow?' he answered 'Earth, water and sun!'

He reads the print directly from his children's books instead of waiting for it to be written out larger on card. Books have become his true passion; he would rather read than spend his hours of free time on the respirator watching televison. If something catches his fancy he roars with laughter, slapping his hand down on the paper. Sometimes he reads aloud or calls my attention to a story worth sharing.

Amanda, who worked as a Montessori teacher encouraged him to thread beads or sew round letters using a darning needle and pieces of cardboard with holes punched into them. 'He's picked this up quickly', she said. 'Most children start with much larger beads, and his sewing's really conscientious.'

'If he uses the abacus,' Dave said, 'he doesn't bother to count the individual beads. He just moves the right number in one go!'

About this time the educational psychologist phoned to give a date for Doran's assessment. I knew that the tests given to brain-injured children were exactly the same as those given to

285

well children and made no allowances for their auditory, visual or manual problems. The results are that such a child will score low in IQ and aptitude, however bright he actually is.

A year ago Doran's daily intelligence programme included French, German and even Russian (from Elvira). He had been given a wide range of general knowledge and a host of words with their definitions. Nevertheless I suspected he would fail to prove himself by official standards. Now whether I liked it or not he was going to become a statistic.

Anna, the district psychologist, was a very perceptive and attractive young woman. She knew nothing about the Institutes' work, but she was prepared to listen. Doran seemed flattered by her attention and eager to please, although this meant nothing unless he could actually hear and see enough to understand her.

The books she had were quite small and the pictures were not always easy for me to make out. She showed him pages divided into four separate illustrations and asked him to identify a word by indicating the drawing that best represented it. The vocabulary increased in sophistication. Before long he was being asked to select pictures to match words, like 'ceremony' and 'assault' together with 'projector' and 'excavator'. He flew blithely along, throwing in the names of some of the other pictures for good measure. The first hesitation came over the word 'bereavement'. 'I've never used it in my life' I said. Anna laughed. In the next test he was expected to indicate what was missing from a series of line drawings of different objects. He got nine out of ten.

Anna paused. 'I'm supposed to stop when he gets six wrong in a row, but he's already well past the average score for his age.'

Doran proceeded to treat her to an impromptu display of his ability to count aloud to twenty. Anna and Doran had now relaxed and were having fun. She took great care to listen to his answers which were emphatic if not always absolutely clear.

'The results are excellent' she said. 'He's well within the normal aptitude for a child of his age. His IQ already reads

286

above average. You'll have no trouble getting him into a normal school when you feel he's ready to go. He should be academically brilliant by then!' 'Don't you find it exciting, Anna?' 'I do' she said. 'Very.'

Amanda decided to celebrate this extraordinary victory by inviting a collection of children to tea. We discovered them one by one on the village recreation ground where they came to play and join in with Doran's running. He was now achieving eight two hundred metre sprints in each of his two miles around the track with distances averaging 1.43 minutes per sprint.

So Doran had a kind of coming-out-into-society party on the lawn. He'd already helped Amanda to mix the chocolate cake which he stirred vigorously from his respirator. Now it was baked and buried under cream and raspberries. He declined the sandwiches with a very polite 'No, thank you' and moved straight into cake. When the children had finished eating and commenced their spontaneous gymnastics on the climbing frame, he stood up and removed his entire set of clothes unaided. After considering his appearance for a moment he replaced his party hat, fixing the elastic carefully under his chin. Then he flexed his biceps and beat his naked chest. 'Big man!' he yelled. 'Doran, is this the new etiquette?' I asked. In answer the embryonic Tarzan rushed wildly round in circles and eventually joined the line of children hanging upside down.

When I discovered that the mother of one of our guests had a sister-in-law with a Down's syndrome daughter, I explained that the Institute had great success with these children and scrambled up to find the book which would explain more fully. Doran ran after me; he was determined to deliver the good news himself. 'He thinks the results are worth the effort' I said. 'The prediction is that he will be a fully-fledged normal ten year-old with his greatest adventure behind him. Though somehow I don't think he'll ever suffer from anticlimax, do you?'

JULY 1984

287